DRUG AFFLICTION

by Dr Ian Oliver

The Robert Gordon University November 2006

Published By
The Robert Gordon University
Aberdeen
AB10 7QB

Main Title: Drug Affliction
Cover Design: The Gatehouse, RGU, Aberdeen
Editor: Dr Ian Oliver

ISBN

CONTENTS

"THERE IS FREEDOM OF CHOICE BUT NO FREEDOM FROM CONSEQUENCES."

FOREWORD

My first experience with illicit drugs was as a young constable in the London, Metropolitan Police at Richmond in 1964. I was in company with a station sergeant on patrol one evening when we arrested a young man for some disorderly conduct. By the standards of the day he had long hair and because of that he stood out from the crowd. As we walked him from George Street to the police station in Paradise Road, I was slightly behind my colleague and the prisoner. I noticed a box of matches fall to the ground from the trousers pocket of the arrested person, and I retrieved it. It did not occur to me that the prisoner might have been disposing of incriminating evidence but I opened the box and found amongst the matches something that looked like a small beef stock cube. I showed it to the station sergeant and neither of us knew for sure that it was cannabis resin but we thought that it might be and so it was sent to the forensic science laboratory for analysis.

In due course, the substance proved to be a compound of cannabis resin and the young man with the long "Beatles" style hair was further charged with possession of an illegal substance and was eventually convicted by the lay magistrates at Richmond Court. Unfortunately, for the prisoner, despite his desperate attempts to appear respectable in a suit and with a 'proper' haircut, the shocked bench sentenced him to six months imprisonment. The Magistrates had no experience of dangerous drugs and they thought that a deterrent and exemplary sentence had to be imposed.

Drugs were talked about in the 1960's and busier police areas had regular dealings with 'purple hearts', cannabis and sinister things called 'reefers' but for the ordinary officer on the beat, these were unusual. Drugs did not have a very high priority in terms of what policing was then thought to be about. Specialists in the Drug or Vice Squads were more likely to deal with them. Gradually drugs became more common but it was not until the late 1970s and early 1980s that non-specialist officers had to deal with drugs on a regular basis.

In 1986, I was awarded a Winston Churchill Travelling Fellowship to visit North America. My intention was to learn more about the drug problem there and specifically to examine some drug education packages, which I had heard about. What I saw in America and Canada excited my interest and I learned about "skills for living" as part of the education of children. Not only did I believe that we in the UK should be adopting some of these teaching methods about drugs, but I saw the great potential that was available for use in places such as Northern Ireland where it was necessary to address the problems of a divided community.

I prepared my report for the Winston Churchill Memorial Trust and sent four copies of it to the policy unit at No. 10 Downing Street. Not long after I was invited to appear on a BBC television programme called "Left, Right and Centre", hosted by Kirsty Wark. There was considerable interest in one of my recommendations:

> "Education (about drugs) cannot start soon enough and although the concentration of effort appears to be necessary for the 12/13 year age group, instruction in kindergarten and at university level is necessary – there must be a continuation of education." (See appendix for full details of recommendations).

I had seen some very effective lessons in Florida given to children as young as five. I was impressed by the considerate and caring way in which foundations were being laid for further and more specific drug awareness training when the children were old enough to understand the nature of the problem. I thought that it would be sensible to consider the possibility of emulating this American approach before our own drug experience in the UK worsened. That proved to be a fond hope.

The then Minister responsible for education in Scotland the late John MacKay (later Lord MacKay) was asked to appear on the same television programme with me. He agreed to do so only on condition that he could be interviewed after me. At that time I had been Chief Constable of Central Scotland Police for six years. When the Minister spoke on the programme he said that what I had suggested was nonsense and that "It will never be government policy to speak about drugs in primary schools".

On 15th September 1986, I held a 'Drugs Education Seminar' for an invited audience of 150 influential people to update them on the current information about dangerous drugs. The Central Regional Council, which was also the Police Authority for the area, banned all head teachers from attending the seminar on the grounds that – "there is not a drug problem in the Region and talking about it is likely to create one". Naturally, the media reporting surrounding the seminar was more concerned with the banning of the head teachers than it was with drugs. At 8.30pm that evening, the BBC Panorama programme showed viewers how to make "crack" cocaine in a microwave oven.

After my experience in North America, I wrote to the Prime Minister, Margaret Thatcher about the need to introduce "skills for living" and drug education across the schools' syllabus as a core subject. I was very careful to say that I had read all of the government published documents and considered all of the Prime Minister's remarks on the subject of drugs. I listed the documents as an appendix to my letter and suggested that there were other areas worthy of further consideration on the subject of drug education. The response that I received about a month later referred me to the very documents that I had listed in my letter.

There is little doubt that what was happening then and what is occurring still with some people is what the Americans refer to as the "denial syndrome". The assertion that no problem exists is a very attractive option because it relieves those who subscribe to that view from the obligation of doing anything. If there is no acknowledged problem then there is no need to address it by training people to tackle it, by spending money to eradicate it, and better still, no blame is attached to anyone for allowing it to develop. Unfortunately, I witnessed many people who denied the problem of alcohol and drugs in schools because they surmised that by acknowledging it, their own professional reputations would be damaged.

I have mentioned these events not to show that I was more aware than others were but because they demonstrate how slow we were to react to the enormous problem of dangerous drugs. When I went to the USA in 1986, many people said that Britain was in the same situation that America had been some 15-20 years previously. Drugs engulfed America in that period and the prediction was that Britain would suffer the same experience only much more rapidly if we did not take positive action. The difference was that drug trafficking had become much more sophisticated and was a major world business. Overproduction of drugs, and an oversupplied market in the USA, had meant that the drug lords in Colombia and elsewhere were targeting Europe and Britain in particular.

The government of the day failed to realise the power and the speed of development of the global trade in drugs. In Britain, too many people refused to believe that we would develop the problems of America. In the ensuing years the UK has become engulfed in drugs and our response to the problem has been disastrously delayed. Too many parents and teachers are "petrified" by drugs and do not know how to react to them; others are still indulging in denial and our overall reactions remain uncoordinated and substantially ineffective.

One other piece of information is relevant to the story of such a deadly delay. On 6th November 1996, I had given the inaugural lecture to the Law Society of the University of Aberdeen. The subject of the lecture had been left to my choice. I was very concerned by the rapidly increasing number of deaths from drug overdoses in the North East of Scotland (30 in 1996), and the relaxed attitudes that seemed to prevail about the topic of drugs. I spoke about the whole problem of drugs and gave some proposals as to what should be done. Included in the lecture was a recommendation that the UK should co-ordinate the fragmented and disparate responses and appoint a UK Anti-Drug Co-ordinator. I sent a copy of my lecture to the Secretary of State for Scotland, Michael Forsyth (now Lord Forsyth) and asked to see him. I received a reply from his assistant diary secretary to say that he was too busy.

Some months later and two weeks before the General Election in 1997 I was asked to contact the Shadow Secretary of State for Scotland George Robertson (now Lord Robertson - former Secretary General of NATO). He informed me that "Tony" was visiting Aberdeen within days and intended announcing a major new initiative against drugs, which would be introduced only in Scotland if Labour won the election. The proposal was that dealing in drugs with pupils within half a mile of a school would be punishable as a new offence. My response was to laugh and I said that this legislation would be next to worthless as most pupils did not obtain drugs from dealers but from their friends. I pointed out that Sheriffs (Magistrates/judges) were very well aware of the problem and that if dealers were targeting pupils the sentences would be very severe and no new offence was necessary.

Immediately I sent a copy of the lecture that I had given to the Law Society by fax to the Shadow Secretary of State. I suggested that if Labour really wanted to address the problem they might wish to think about appointing an Anti – Drug Co-ordinator for the UK. The following day, the Shadow Home Secretary Jack Straw announced that when Labour formed a government a UK Anti-Drug Co-ordinator would be appointed. What happened was that a 'Parliamentary adviser' was appointed on a three year contract; he was more commonly referred to as the 'Drug Czar'; in March 2000 that contract was extended by the Prime Minister but the co-ordinator later resigned. No one was appointed to replace him as the then Home Secretary David Blunkett wanted to handle the problem himself.

Sadly, the problem of drugs is worsening and this book sets out to do several things. Firstly, it is intended to provide accurate information for everyone who ought to know about drugs and their effects. Secondly, it addresses some of the more common subjects in the debate such as "harm reduction" and "legalisation" and attempts to explain them in some detail. Thirdly, it offers some proposals about what more needs to be done to make the global and international reaction to drugs more effective, as well as offering some suggestions for the UK. What the book does not do is provide all there is to know about drugs. It is intended to be a helpful and informative document for anyone who wishes to know about a subject that affects all of us in one way or another.

PREFACE TO "DRUG AFFLICTION"

The global retail market for illicit drugs is estimated to be in excess of US$320 billion annually and this figure exceeds the GDPs of nearly 90% of the countries in the world (United Nations World Drug Report 2005). Profits for the traffickers are enormous and with the availability of such vast sums of money they are able to use them in many different and nefarious ways that impact on the lives of almost everyone without them necessarily being aware of it.

The adverse global effects are significant and drug money is used to fund organised crime, international terrorism and the trade is the cause of major global public health problems. Additionally, between 50-70% of UK domestic crimes are thought to be drug related. Europe imports approximately 33% of the global supply of all illicit drugs while the UK takes a significant share of this and consequently has one of the worst drug problems in Europe. Additionally the UK has a very high rate of the spread of sexually transmitted and blood borne diseases such as AIDS/HIV and Hepatitis C. AIDS/HIV is spreading at a rate faster than the authorities are able to respond and for example, it is estimated that in sub-Saharan Africa up to 25% of the workforce will die from these infections in the next decade. A similar pattern of tragedy is developing in Asia and Russia which will exceed that in Africa by 2010. In the case of Hepatitis C, much of which is spread through the sharing of equipment by intravenous drug users (IDUs) but not exclusively, the World Health Organisation has called this a global pandemic and this disease will be the cause of the greatest demand for liver transplants in the UK this decade.

These statistics are disquieting and they demonstrate a huge potential for continually compounding and rapidly developing harms to society if we fail to take significant and urgent steps to combat the spread of the drugs trade and the associated crimes.

Despite this terrible situation the UK Government has failed to deal with the enormity of the problem and the debilitating effects of dangerous drugs in a comprehensive manner. From a position of attempting to reduce both the supply of and the demand for illicit drugs it has gradually and almost subliminally moved to a policy of 'pragmatism' that accepts that drugs are freely available and are too difficult to eliminate without the expenditure of large sums of money. The National Criminal Intelligence Service estimated that not less than 40 tonnes of heroin and 40 tonnes of cocaine enter the UK unchecked every year (this estimate was confirmed in "The UK Threat Assessment of Serious Organised Crime for 2006/7 by The Serious Organised Crime Agency [SOCA]); additionally there are amphetamine type substances and cannabis, both of which are imported in bulk and domestically produced.

An attractive sounding, but seriously debilitating policy of Harm Reduction has been adopted without much formal consideration but which is a term that has been hi-jacked by those who favour the legalisation of drugs and who use it unashamedly to convince people, and particularly policy makers, that we must accept the fact of drugs and find ways of minimising the harmful effects of extensive use (frequently this tactic is a cover for promoting the idea of legalising drug use). Indeed, even the Education Inspectorate in England & Wales, OFSTED appears to have been seduced into accepting this position by stating that "the key aim of drug education is to make healthy informed choices" instead of following the position declared by the Home Affairs Select Committee on Drugs that education in schools should be against drugs. "Informed choices" is the language of the legalisers who wish to teach children how to take drugs safely when the only safe and correct message must be that all drug use is dangerous unless under medical advice and guidance.

Treatment for those most affected by drug dependence is seriously under funded and too few residential places are immediately available.

Another example of the decline into a policy of pragmatism is to be found in our Prison System where research by the Prison Reform Trust and the National Aids Trust has indicated that many UK prisons are failing effectively to provide adequate healthcare for prisoners with hepatitis C and HIV. Over half the prisons in England and Wales are reported to have no sexual health policy despite the fact that hepatitis C levels are 20 times higher than the rate in the general public and 9% of male inmates and 11% of females are infected. HIV rates in male prisoners are 15 times higher than those of men not in jail. The study found "inconsistent and often sub-standard healthcare" in our prisons combined with overcrowding and frequent movement of prisoners which contributes to the potential for the spread of the diseases both within and outside the prisons. In other words, UK policy has allowed our prisons to become incubators for infection and the spread of diseases at great risk to the health of the general public and individual prisoners. However, the proposed remedies are equally dangerous propositions in that members of the Trusts advocated the distribution of clean needles and disinfecting tablets within prisons when drug use in prisons is illegal. Additionally it has been proposed in Scotland that prisoners who were heroin users before imprisonment should be "re-toxified" with a course of methadone (a more addictive substance than heroin itself) immediately before release as a pragmatic way of reducing the possibility of overdose when the prisoners revert to former drug taking habits after release. The sensible and desirable policy should be to ensure that no drugs are available within prisons and the period of custody should be used to aid drug using prisoners to achieve abstinence and detoxification.

A similar development has occurred with Needle Exchange Programmes (NEPs) which were adopted in the UK in the mid-1980s as a pragmatic approach to stopping the spread of blood borne diseases by making clean needles available to IDUs. Recent research by the Health Protection Agency has drawn attention to the fact that the inappropriate distribution of needles from what have been admitted to be "needle-give-aways" has apparently failed to reduce the spread of diseases amongst IDUs. A report issued by the Agency at the end of 2005 revealed significant increases in infections such as hepatitis C and hepatitis A and B among IDUs and that 50% of them were unaware that they had become infected.

In the case of Methadone Maintenance programmes the Government has presided over a situation where addicts are "maintained" on a highly addictive substance for extraordinarily long periods of time without any realistic attempt to assist patients to achieve abstinence. Under the correct supervision and guidance Methadone treatment can be a very effective way of assisting abstinence but the reality is the continuation of prescribed methadone without much attempt to provide the additional and necessary assistance to come off heroin. Many of those maintained on methadone use their supply as a crutch and are also on street drugs.

Unfortunately we have allowed a culture of tolerance and acceptance of drugs in society to develop to the point where those who are not directly involved with drug related problems consider that the issue has little to do with them. There is a distinct and dangerous absence of awareness about the extent to which drugs have a serious impact on our society compounded by determined efforts on the part of the drug traffickers and legalisers to spread false and misleading information about drugs in order to promote the trade and to deceive people into believing that there is a safe way to take illicit drugs. There is little appropriate training for professionals and most people are left to gain their inadequate knowledge about drugs from media hype and so called "street wisdom", which is seriously deficient and frequently dangerously inaccurate. Regrettably there is very little in the way of high profile public health education that would enable people to become fully aware of the dangers that are associated with illicit drug use. In fact the UK Government may be criticised for sending out mixed messages and conflicting signals about its position on drugs and an absolutely unacceptable position has been the announcement by a Home Secretary of his intentions about the amount of drugs that an individual may possess before being adjudged a dealer.

Only 20% of UK businesses have a meaningful anti-drug policy when the impact of drugs in the workplace is significant and dangerous. Additionally, it is estimated that at least £10 billion annually is lost to business because people use this much of their disposable income in supporting their drug habits.

The enormous problem of illicit drugs is likely to be made worse by the fact that many are advocating their legalisation because the so-called "War on Drugs" has been lost and the money 'wasted' on the war should be used for the 'betterment of society'. A moment's consideration should demonstrate the nonsense of this proposition and yet it is gaining ground because drugs have become classified as "too difficult to deal with" and pragmatic policies combined with Harm Reduction are the only answer.

Clearly it seems time for a major review of Government policy on illicit drugs and this view is reinforced by criticism contained in a report by The House of Commons Science and Technology Committee in July 2006 ("Drug Classification: making a hash of it? HC1031 31.07.06). The Committee observed that *"the weakness of the evidence base on addiction and drug abuse is a severe hindrance to effective policy making..."* and urged the Government to increase significantly its investment in research

Drugs will be with us for a very long period of time unless active Government initiatives of public education and a commitment to stop tolerating illicit drugs are adopted together with immediately available treatment for those who need it. Currently, there is little sign that this is happening and there is a clear need to address drugs and the associated problems of Organised Crime, Terrorism and serious Public Health issues. It is about these matters that this book is concerned.

INTRODUCTION

Drugs and drug dependency have been with us for many centuries but at the beginning of a new millennium there is significant, voluntary use and abuse of substances around the world, which is alarming. In 2005, the United Nations Office for Drugs and Crime (UNODC) estimated that perhaps 200 million people globally indulge in the abuse of illicit drugs. The total includes over 160 million marijuana users, 16 million opiate users (including an estimated 11 million heroin users), and 14 million cocaine users. According to the UN's Annual Drug Report the global drug trade is worth at least $320 billion, a figure larger than the gross domestic product of 90 percent of the nations on the planet.

Wars have been fought about opium and governments and criminals have used the drug trade to great financial advantage but now, such is the tolerance and acceptance of drugs combined with ignorance and misinformation, that nations are in danger of being overwhelmed by the power, which is drug trafficking. There is too a great fear amongst parents that they are helpless to keep their children from the dangers of drug abuse.

The British Prime Minister, Tony Blair spoke publicly of being "petrified" by drugs and he expressed a determination to deal with the problem in a way in which governments have failed to do in the past ("This Morning" TV Programme Sep.1999). Despite this declaration, the Prime Minister failed to include dealing with the drug problem as one of the five 'great goals' for the New Labour Party during the 21st Century (The Times 28.2.00). No clear and adequate policy has emerged which has proved to be the panacea to a plague that has engulfed whole countries and even continents and which is the cause of so much human misery and such waste of economic resources. Indeed, several European countries have introduced policies which are tantamount to the legalisation of cannabis. Canada has shown a similar inclination to permit prescription of 'medical marijuana' much to the annoyance of the USA, as has The Netherlands. It has been reported that from 2006 Canadians who want to use marijuana for medical purposes will be able to purchase the drug at select pharmacies. Health Canada planned to let certified medical-marijuana patients get their drugs from pharmacies in a similar way to a system that was permitted in The Netherlands. This will change the system whereby drugs grown by a government contractor are distributed by courier to 237 authorised patients. Some patients were authorised to grow their own supplies under certain restrictions. Health Canada planned to offer specialist training to some pharmacists to facilitate this policy. However, there are indications that a new Conservative Government may change this position.

The drug trade, which according to UN estimates represents between 8-10% of world trade, is linked with crime and terrorism, world wide financial crises, and the spread of illness and disease, in a way that is almost too large to comprehend. The social consequences are enormous for people who individually are powerless to combat the disaster. Millions of people are affected by drugs either as users or as producers whose livelihoods depend on the continuation of the trade; others devote their whole lives to the criminal activities promoted by drug trafficking. Money laundering has an enormous effect on global business. There can be few people in the world whose lives are not touched in some way by drugs although many of them may not be aware of this.

It is also true that millions of people choose to believe that drugs are no concern of theirs and they deny that they are affected. Ignorance is widespread even amongst those whose direct responsibility it is to address the problem, and this is compounded by false information deliberately spread by some of those who wish to legalise drugs.

In the last decade, the availability of dangerous drugs has increased to such a point that almost any person who wishes to acquire cannabis or 'crack' cocaine would have little difficulty in locating a supplier and, in most cases, the price would be affordable although many who have become dependent on drugs have turned to crime to pay for their habit. The purity levels of heroin and cocaine have risen significantly in recent years, often as high as 90% but a report from the Office of National Drug Control Policy in the USA claims that their anti-drug initiatives in Latin America have resulted in significant reduction in purity levels in both cocaine and the heroin that is produced there (National Drug Control Strategy 2006)

Clearly, the criminal justice system has failed to bring about much reduction in demand and despite enormous international co-operation and the expenditure of billions of dollars in combating drug trafficking across the globe, the amount of seizures compared with production of illicit drugs is pathetically small. The rewards of this trade are so huge and the organisation of criminal enterprises over many years has been so successful that it is foolhardy to believe that law enforcement alone can have any significant impact on drugs.

In most western countries the demand for drugs has blossomed rapidly. The culture of tolerance and acceptance amongst the younger generation is widespread, even with those who have no personal desire to use drugs. The traditional opinion formers in society have been wrong-footed and left to look on in horror and amazement as their children and grandchildren argue the case for a liberalisation in attitudes. Others have been persuaded to believe that legalisation or decriminalisation of dangerous drugs would, in some undefined way, alleviate an enormous social problem.

The older generation has come to realise only recently the significance of this blight on society and many are at a loss to know what to do about it. The reaction to drugs has been fragmented and generally uncoordinated and "while Rome burns" the problem is compounded and grows in power and influence at increasing cost to everyone.

CHAPTER 1
Perceptions of the drug problem and the proposed remedies.

Public recognition of the enormity of the problems caused by drug trafficking is limited although there has been official acknowledgement of the damaging effect that the drug trade is having in so many areas of our lives. Many people work hard to draw the drug problem to public attention and provide help where it is needed, nevertheless there has been insufficient government action to ensure proper public awareness and adequate treatment for those who become dependent on drugs.

There are many professional people, including doctors, health and social workers, police, prison officers, and teachers who ought to know a great deal more about the effects of drugs than they do. Few training programmes for professional qualifications encompass the necessary information and the majority of the members of the public are left to gain what little knowledge they can from the media. This is often limited and sometimes wildly inaccurate information presented to a largely uninformed audience.

Governments either independently or through the combined activities of organisations like the United Nations have spent billions of dollars in various schemes aimed at combating or reducing the trade; the UNODC estimate in 2003 was $50 billion compared with $500 billion against tobacco abuse (Progress Report on the mid-term review of UNGASS by the Executive Director, 8.4.03 UNODC/ED/2). The USA spends considerably more than this total annually in its own anti-drug activities and in its policy document for 2004 the US Office of National Drug Control Policy showed that the US spends at least $160 billion annually. This assessment includes the costs of law enforcement, environmental impact and the treatment of addiction. Nevertheless, most citizens and the average politician remain blissfully unaware of how serious an issue illicit drugs has become and the enormity of the threat to stability that they pose. It is almost as if some political leaders are in a state of "denial" that a significant and hugely damaging problem exists; it seems that many regard the problem as too difficult to eliminate and are content to tolerate and accept drug abuse as a feature of the modern world.

Policy documents have been published by some governments, which seem to lack much sense of urgency and commitment to defeating the illicit drug problem. This may have resulted in the spreading of an apparently permissive culture towards personal use of illicit drugs and the undermining of the efforts to curb the supply in countries where illicit drug raw materials originate. For example, in April 1999 a law was passed in Portugal stipulating that drug abusers would face civil fines rather than jail sentences. Under the new law the abuse and possession of drugs for personal use is no longer a criminal offence but is treated administratively (INCB Annual Report 1999 and

Portuguese Drug Strategy 22.4.99 - An evaluation of this was due to be published in 2005). The International Narcotics Control Board stressed that it regarded this move by Portugal as being contrary to the line followed in international drug control treaties, which require that drug use should be limited to medical and scientific purposes and that States and parties should make drug possession a criminal offence. However, the Board acknowledged that the exercise of criminal jurisdiction is discretionary and that Governments may provide offenders with alternatives to conviction and punishment. Several other European countries have adopted policies which make the possession of small amounts of drugs for personal use, administrative or civil offences, not involving a criminal sanction.

In 2003, the High Court of Canada directed that marijuana packages should be supplied to doctors who might wish to dispense this for seriously ill patients much to the dismay of the medical profession and anti-drug campaigners. This was followed in 2005 by the preliminary authorisation of the use of oral mouth sprays derived from the cannabis plant, called Sativex, as a treatment for neuropathic pain among multiple sclerosis patients (Wall Street Journal 08.02.05), and the announcement by Health Canada that it intended to authorise certain pharmacists to distribute marijuana for medical purposes to 237 certified medical - marijuana patients.

A failure by some Governments to send out clear messages against drug abuse leads to confusion and misunderstanding in the most vulnerable sectors of the population. This was particularly noticeable in the UK 2002/3 after the Home Secretary indicated a determination to reclassify cannabis and the result was that many came to regard that substance as being relatively harmless. In terms of law enforcement the UK has concentrated on dealing with 'Class A' drugs such as heroin and cocaine, and has neglected cannabis at a time when world production and abuse is increasing. (Cannabis was downgraded from Class B to Class C on 29th January 2004).

The British Government's decision to downgrade cannabis to a Class C drug was criticised by executive director of the UN Office on Drugs and Crime (UNODC), Antonio Maria Costa, who said that countries got the "drug problem they deserved" if they maintained inadequate policies. In an unusual statement, he suggested cannabis was as harmful as cocaine and heroin - a stance which differs widely from the British attitude of treating cannabis far less seriously than Class A substances.

Although he did not specifically name and shame the UK, Mr Costa said at the Washington DC launch of the UNODC's 2006 World Drug Report: "Policy reversals leave young people confused as to just how dangerous cannabis is. With cannabis-related health damage increasing, it is fundamentally wrong for countries to make cannabis control dependent on which party is in government. The cannabis pandemic, like other challenges to public health, requires consensus, a consistent commitment across the political spectrum and by society at large." Mr Costa suggested that cannabis was now "considerably more potent" than a few decades ago and that it was a "mistake" to dismiss it as a soft, relatively harmless drug. "Today, the harmful characteristics of cannabis are no longer that different from those of other plant-based drugs such as cocaine and heroin," Mr Costa said. The report estimated 162million people used cannabis at least once in 2004, the equivalent of four per cent of the 15 to 64-year-old global population.

This is not to say that all involvement with drugs requires a criminal sanction. Treatment, rehabilitation, after-care, and social reintegration all have a place as alternatives as well as demand reduction by way of education. However, some take the view that failure to apply some criminal sanctions where appropriate sends out "mixed messages" to a largely uninformed, confused and vulnerable public.

It seems that some policies are designed to give token lip service to addressing the issue while others give an extravagant description of what will be done, without the financial backing and with little real commitment. No co-ordinated and thorough analysis has been undertaken to understand the full extent of the global problem, to define it, or to discover appropriate international remedies. In most cases the policies are 'selfish' and lack the altruism and multilateralism that is necessary to tackle this massive, world problem (see section on comparison between US. and British policy documents). This problem was recognised in the mid-term review of UNGASS (see later) when UNODC declared its intention to seek more reliable data from countries.

In the absence of meaningful international co-ordination those people who see advantage in promoting the idea of "freedom of choice" and legalisation of drugs, have been very active in advocating these beliefs. The people who are likely to be most affected are often incredibly ignorant about drugs, which will almost certainly touch some members of their families during their developing years when they are most vulnerable and susceptible to harm.

Parents and teachers who are equally as concerned by drugs as the Prime Minister often hide behind the claim that their children or pupils know more about the subject than they do. Instead of seeking out the information that will both inform them and their children and which would alleviate much of the concern, they accept the result of this posture, which is that not enough accurate and informed debate and guidance is occurring in homes or schools. If children are left to become "street-wise" they may find that particular form of wisdom to be seriously deficient.

There are some good education programmes in use in some schools but there is much more that must be done if we are to hope to have any impact on the rapidly changing culture that accepts drugs in all societies. There are also some very damaging packages which run the risk of promoting drug use because they support the idea of 'harm reduction', sometimes in ignorance of the fact that this term has been usurped by those seeking to legalise drugs. Drugs are a major factor in our everyday lives and they should be dealt with as a core and essential part of every educational curriculum.

The House of Commons, Home Affairs Select Committee pointed up its concern about the quality of some drug education materials (Report 2002) and the possibility of ambiguous messages contained in them. The Committee was of the opinion that all drugs education material should be based on the premise that any drug use can be harmful and should be discouraged, but this stance seems hardly adequate. If the government is determined to eradicate, or reduce to a minimum, the dangers of extensive drug abuse, and if it expects to prevent its "normalisation", then a more positive and determined strategy seems to be necessary.

Such analysis of the drug problem as there is has been often fragmented and no international inter-government forum has encompassed its full extent in a way that has resulted in a totally united global approach. For many years, the approach was that drugs are a criminal justice problem and where that has been found to be not entirely accurate the public health dimension has been introduced with a pragmatic approach to 'harm reduction'.

Either from a perverse perception of personal liberty or, as a result of failing to recognise any realistic way of overcoming an enormous and pandemic problem, the legalisation and decriminalisation arguments have found fertile ground. Some cling to a naïve belief that such policies would "take the profits out of the drug trade" while others pursue that argument in order to promote the social acceptability of drugs for their own reasons. The supply and demand perception is also one which many find to be attractive – if we can reduce the supply the demand will fall and if we can reduce the demand there will be no ready market for the drugs and production will have to fall; regrettably this view has been demonstrated to be too simplistic.

This logic fails to recognise that such remedies cannot be achieved instantaneously and that collateral damage will occur to those who have come to depend on the growing of the coca bush or poppy crops for their survival. Many incomplete and sometimes illogical models are put forward with a variety of remedies.

Internationally there has been a lack of corporate focus on the significance of the dangers associated with substance abuse and this has resulted in much of the reaction being fragmented or distorted by inaccurate perceptions of current difficulties. Local reactions are often driven by the immediacy of personal or community tragedy – a young life is lost to drugs or a community has been blighted by dealers – and the well intentioned but uncoordinated responses are often dissipated and sometimes achieve little in terms of an enduring remedy.

Internationally, some drug crop eradication policies have been unsuccessful because they have not been thought through adequately. World markets have not been assessed properly, commodity prices have collapsed, and social unrest, mainly in Latin American countries, has been widespread to the point of toppling governments because of clumsy and inadequate approaches to the problem. Where plans have been well considered there is evidence that alternative development can be a successful contribution to reducing the supply of drugs. The root consideration with botanical narcotic drugs is the poverty of small farmers whose meagre livelihoods depend upon selling products for which there is a significant demand that guarantees income. Unfortunately, there is an overwhelming demand for illicit drugs, and many alternative crops are not so easily marketed.

Frequently opposition to the drug trade has been large numbers of differently motivated groups operating independently of one another; sometimes in ignorance of others, sometimes in competition for inadequate funding or resources but almost always ending in some wasted or duplicated efforts. The wheel is being reinvented so many times with little significant impact on a global problem of enormous dimensions. The drug trade is richly funded and organised but the opposition is frequently well intentioned, uncoordinated and often ineffective. The United Nations Office on Drugs and Crimes is a small organisation with a very limited budget whereas in contrast both the traffickers and the lobbies proposing liberalisation and drug-receptive lifestyles enjoy budgets that are many times greater.

There is failure to fund and implement a multi-faceted approach for dealing with a long-term problem which is unlikely ever to be completely eradicated. The best that can be hoped for is effective management and control based upon the three-pronged strategy of intelligence-led and targeted enforcement, appropriate education across the social and professional spectrum, and adequate, readily available treatment and support for those who need it. Naturally there is also a continuing need to research and address the causes and reasons why so many people choose to use and abuse illicit drugs. There is a need to eliminate some of the social deficiencies that seem to result in some people turning to mind-altering substances as a relief from their despair.

The Criminal Justice Approach.

For nearly a century, the United States of America have been fighting a "Drug War" although that description has not always found favour. The USA has suffered the ravages of drugs from a 'user' perspective more than any other western country. Despite all of its dedication and the expenditure of billions of dollars both at home and abroad, it has failed, so far, to reduce the problem of dangerous and illicit drugs to manageable proportions.

The primary motivation behind US policy was based originally on the criminal justice approach in which the aim was to interdict the criminal traffickers and suppliers and to prevent drugs from entering the US market. In addition to this approach, there have been other sophisticated policies, which have embraced all of the other methods thought appropriate for dealing with the problem. In terms of the worst scenario, the US can claim some major successes in reducing the number of drug users that existed in the seventies in the aftermath of the Vietnam War. Official estimates indicated that in 1971 as many as 15-20% of the low-ranking enlisted personnel, were heroin users – that represents a figure of between 25-37000 people. In the 1970s it was estimated that there were 26 million regular drug users in the USA; by the 1990s that figure had been reduced to an estimated 13.5 million. The "Just Say No" strategy, which is now so frequently maligned, had been very successful, but the reduction was not all due to organised resistance. There is evidence which shows that the non-availability of heroin at that time meant that some people stopped their drug using habits. Some have argued that this form of prohibition was very effective and this is why targeted law enforcement is seen as an important part of any anti-drug strategy.

Nevertheless, despite some enterprising and original approaches to the problem, it remains and continues to be a major drain on the country's resources and a tremendously damaging blight on the future development of that nation.

In December 1989 President Bush (Snr.) authorised the invasion of Panama by 24000 combat troops with the specific intention of capturing General Manuel Noriega, a Caribbean drug trafficker, who was eventually taken to Miami, indicted for drug crimes and is now serving forty years imprisonment in the USA. That expensive and questionably legal exercise had no real impact on the flow of drugs into the USA and neither did it frighten off other drug lords in Latin-America. Panama remains a major money-laundering and cocaine transhipment centre.

The following year the Attorney General announced that federal prosecutors had filed an indictment against another world drug lord, Khun Sa, who operated the opium trade in Burma and who was described as "the most powerful drug trafficker in the Golden Triangle" (New York Times - 16.3.90). Extradition proceedings were unsuccessful but the President presumably did not consider sending a combat force to Asia where the consequences of such action would have provoked massive, international opposition.

In Colombia and other Latin American countries in the US 'back-yard' where the Americans and others including the UK have given "advice" and training, the strategy has been one of determined enforcement. Thousands of Colombians are killed in the narco-terrorist war annually. The Anti-Narcotics Police reported a 20% casualty rate together with the loss of 6 US supplied helicopters shot down by terrorists in 1998. The military reported 500 casualties in 1998 and at the height of the operations against Escobar's Medellin Cartel, the Colombian National Police saw 1100 officers killed in one year.

Throughout the country, various businesses hired their own private armies trained by former international members of various Special Forces, including American, Russian and British, for protection against the terrorists and drug lords. The controversial "Plan Colombia" resulted in the expenditure of millions of US dollars in what was described as potentially another Vietnam. Colombia remains a major drug supplier and the enforcement problems continue.

The US policy towards its neighbour Mexico has been extremely difficult. The 2000 miles of border with the USA is as porous as that between Afghanistan and its neighbours. Despite massive efforts at interdiction, the reality demonstrates the impossibility of winning the drug war by law enforcement methods alone. It is likely that less than 10% of the estimated amount of drugs entering the USA is intercepted by law enforcement agents. Mexican drug barons have taken the place of their Latin American suppliers but both groups remain hugely problematical and the drug flow continues largely unabated.

That estimate of seizures is probably true for every other country in the world. Logistically it is impossible to search every person, vehicle, ship, or aircraft entering the USA. In 1998 278 million people, 86 million cars and 40000 trucks and rail cars entered the US from Mexico and the establishment of a free-trade zone without the border controls was viewed by many as a highly dangerous and damaging proposal. The argument put forward was that if this were to occur then the whole of the North American continent would become wide open to uninhibited cocaine, heroin and other drug supplies from Latin America and elsewhere.

In his testimony to the US Senate Foreign Relations Committee, in October 1997, a retired special agent, from the DEA's office in Houston, Texas, said –

" ...every indicator, now and over the last twenty years reveals the government of Mexico consistently works together with the major drug-trafficking families, seeing to it that the drugs ...are offloaded securely, protected, shipped cross-country under convoy, stored and safely transported to our border"

(Donald Ferrarone, former DEA Agent in Houston and Thailand,
in testimony to US Senate Foreign Relations Committee,
October 1997. See also Appendix to Chapter 1).

The law enforcement difficulties faced by the USA are replicated around the world in varying degrees. Not every country will experience the scale of the American problem but proportionately, the result is likely to be the same. The supply of drugs will not be reduced significantly by law enforcement methods alone although it is vitally important that intelligence is collected and law enforcement agencies continue to play their role in combating the drug problem by interdicting and disrupting supplies and arresting the major suppliers.

Significantly, after the terrorist attacks in the USA on 11th September 2001, the American Government made defence against terrorist attacks its highest priority and this was at the expense of its anti-drug activities around the globe. DEA agents were withdrawn from important areas so that law enforcement could re-deploy limited resources and personnel in its war on terrorism. However, it has to be mentioned that there is an extremely strong link between many global terrorist organisations and the drug trade

(see statement of Steven W. Casteel - Assistant Administrator for Intelligence {DEA}
before the Senate Committee on the Judiciary May 20 2003).

Less than 10% of all illicit drugs shipments are likely to be intercepted. The financial power of the drug lords is such that they are able to buy the most sophisticated equipment in order to ply their trade. The rewards for everyone involved are huge and there are many people prepared to take significant risks to get rich. Corruption is rife and if that fails, the drug lords are prepared to kill anyone who gets in their way.It was reported in "The Times" (1.12.99), that the mass graves of up to 100 missing persons, 22 believed to be American citizens and the remainder Mexican, were identified in Mexico, near Cuidad Juarez. The bodies are thought to be those of victims of the Mexican drug cartel responsible for shipping Colombian cocaine into the US.

These alleged atrocities were investigated by a team of Mexican Federal Police and American FBI officers; an informer is reported to have alleged that local Mexican police assisted the drug lords in assassinating people who had crossed the cartel. It is believed that people who have been missing for up to ten years may have been buried at the location and that these graves represent a series of killings rather than one mass murder. Two of the bodies were identified as those of DEA and FBI agents.

According to the Office of National Drug Control Policy, in 1996 the cost of drug trafficking to the United States was estimated to be: -

- 100,000 deaths recorded and $300 billion spent in the 1990s;

- 500,000 new emergency room cases per annum;

- 250,000 Americans serving time for drug related offences;

drugs had been used in at least 1/3rd homicides, assaults, and property crimes.

In the United Kingdom up to 70% of acquisitive crime is thought to be in some way, drug related.

The Public Health Approach:

Many people argue that drugs are a public health issue and a matter of personal choice in the same way as alcohol and tobacco. Those who are unfortunate enough to require treatment for drug related afflictions should receive medical attention in the same way that those who smoke or drink alcohol are treated. Those who support this thinking fail to acknowledge that this approach would create more dependent people and would place an enormous additional burden on the health services as well as diverting attention away from people who do not have a self-induced condition. (NB, a growing pressure in the UK occurred in June 2003 when it was suggested that those who present self-induced health problems to the NHS should be required to pay extra for their treatment and enter into a contract to live healthy lives. This argument continued to grow and was raised once more in 2006).

A move from punishment, to treatment, has been advocated for the following reasons: -

- Prohibition causes higher prices for illicit drugs which in turn encourages that trade; (generally world prices have fallen in the last decade)

- Interdiction against producers is seldom successful and merely displaces production to another location – e.g. a 56% reduction of coca crops in Peru resulted in a 25% increase in production in Colombia; (US. ONDCP. 1999, International Narcotics Control Board Annual Report 1999).

- Imprisonment and punishment is unsuccessful as a deterrent because of the high recidivism rate, particularly amongst heroin and cocaine users.

In October 2000, Drug Testing & Treatment Orders (DTTOs) became a sentencing option in England & Wales. The DTTOs, inspired by American Drug Courts became part of the Government's ten-year strategy for addressing drug misuse "Tackling Drugs to Build a Better Britain". A DTTO gives courts power to add a requirement for drug treatment to a probation order. It is a demanding and resource intensive order that can last between 6 months to three years. It differs from an existing probation order in that the court checks progress and compliance. Mandatory urine testing takes place at specified intervals and sentence plans may change in response to either progress or problems.

Seductive catch phrases such as 'healing without harm' have been used in the campaign to adopt a public health approach, which is sometimes used as a cover for those who wish to legalise drugs.

For many years it has been argued that drugs should be regarded as entirely a matter for the health authorities. If someone became dependent upon drugs then the remedy was thought to be that he/she should go to the doctor for treatment or, in extreme cases, attend a detoxification clinic.

In the 1960s, a medical approach for people who had become dependent upon hard drugs was adopted in the UK. Some patients were treated by prescription of the very drug upon which they had become dependent, in a controlled way. More recently, the prescription of methadone as a heroin substitute has resulted in problems. A small survey on methadone maintenance schemes conducted by a national charity, in Manchester and Liverpool, added to the serious doubts about the wisdom behind this approach. There are mixed views about the efficacy of this form of treatment and a recent report on a similar approach in Switzerland has called into question its effectiveness

(Report of the External Expert committee of the World Health Organisation 1999).

The International Narcotics Control Board went further and observed that it was concerned over the Swiss heroin programme and that it did not encourage other Governments to allow heroin to be prescribed to opiate addicts. The INCB drew attention to responsibilities under the international drug control treaties and clearly viewed the Swiss experiment as coming close to being in breach of international agreements.

(INCB Annual Report 1999).

Despite official opposition to prescribing heroin to addicted/dependent persons, and the evidence of the failure of similar experiments, the House of Commons Select Committee on Home Affairs recommended in its report in May 2002 that heroin should be made available in safe-injecting houses. The report estimated over 250,000 people in the UK known to be dependent on heroin. The British Medical Association opposed prescribing heroin for several reasons, not least of which was the estimated cost of £15K per annum for each person.

The recommendation was made because the Committee was impressed by reports of allegedly successful, Swiss Heroin Trials which were criticised as being scientifically unsound by a Committee of medical experts under the auspices of the World Health Organisation. In 2003, the UK Government stated that it would introduce the prescription of heroin to a limited number of dependent persons - probably fewer than 400 - and that certain doctors would be given training in this form of treatment.

As the abuse of drugs increased in the UK in particular, and as the spread of blood-borne diseases such as AIDS/HIV and Hepatitis C increased, a policy of harm reduction was followed as a pragmatic approach in preventing an epidemic. Needle Exchange Programmes (NEPs) were introduced for intravenous drug users combined with the giving of advice about safe practices. In the USA, Federal funding is not applied to such programmes. (See later).

Gradually the idea of "harm reduction" and "harm minimisation" became entangled with the move for the legalisation of drugs and as there is no standard and universally accepted definition of these terms, some confusion has grown up, particularly in the field of formal education. (See chapter on Education). Certainly, those who wish to see drugs legalised have used the 'harm reduction' approach as a way of seducing others into accepting that drugs are an inevitable feature of modern life. They have argued that instead of wasting resources on prevention and supply/demand reduction, governments should legalise drugs and teach people how to make 'informed choices' and to use illicit drugs 'sensibly and safely'.

In the United States, critics of what they have called "the war on drugs", point to the fact that many federal law enforcement and other agencies are involved in interdiction, at great cost to the taxpayer. These agencies include: - Departments of State, Defence, Treasury, Agriculture and Criminal Justice; the CIA, DEA, FBI, US Customs, Border Patrol, US Forest Service, Bureau of Land Management, ATF, Coast Guard, National Guard and 4 Intelligence Centres; in the case of financial crimes, and money laundering other agencies such as FinCen. (Financial Crimes Enforcement Network), and the Federal Reserve Bank are involved. The Department of Homeland Security formed after the terrorist attack on 11th September 2001 is also much concerned with the link between drugs and terrorism.

The argument proposes that by treating illicit drug abuse as a public health problem then the resources that are "wasted" on enforcement policies could be used to treat those who need help.

Whilst treatment is a highly desirable adjunct to dealing with the problem of drugs, it is not a stand-alone answer and unfortunately the resources and appropriately trained personnel have not been made available to cope with the growing demand. Any policy relying solely on one answer to a problem is bound to fail.

Supply and Demand.

The logic behind the market approach to the drug problem is too simple on its own to be of any value in countering the difficulties that have arisen over many years. The argument put forward is that a saleable product will find a ready market. If there were no demand for drugs the traffickers, suppliers and growers would not waste their time in servicing a poor market.

Examples from history are used to reinforce the point – e.g. the decline in alcoholism during the years of Prohibition in the USA, and the way in which drug addiction in the USA declined during the Second World War and immediately after Vietnam, because supplies of heroin were not readily available.

Clearly, there is some truth in this logic and the argument is one that has been used by Latin-American countries when they have been pressurised by the USA to eradicate crops or to counteract the suppliers. However, the use and abuse of drugs has become so widespread and the dependency of many people and countries on drug production has become so great that it is no longer solely a question of either cutting the supply or of reducing the demand. These things cannot be achieved in isolation and they cannot be secured overnight. The drug problem has become so huge and so interconnected with other factors that it has become necessary to produce a composite and co-ordinated answer.

To be effective, supply reduction depends upon international agreement and co-operation between governments and law enforcement agencies. Universal agreement has proved to be impossible. Not only has corruption become a very powerful inhibitor to effective enforcement but also the philosophical approaches adopted by various governments in their responses to what are viewed by some as a costly and intractable problem have resulted in a lack of total commitment.

The demand reduction argument relies on the efficacy of public health education programmes, which should give people sufficient information to discourage the desire to experiment with any substance that may result in dependency. Unfortunately, there has been little agreement on the best form of education. There has been a significant and damaging attempt to promote the view that because all pupils will be exposed to drugs and some may be tempted to use them, then education should include information on how to use drugs 'safely'.

An additional problem has been that many people whose work brings them into contact with drugs are not fully aware of the global nature and the full extent of the issue. There is a clear need for education about drugs within professional circles and with many parents who are both concerned about the problem and unaware of how to discuss the matter within the families for fear that young people know more about drugs than they do. This latter point applies with many teachers as well. Again, the point has to be made that it would be unwise to rely on just one anti-drug strategy, as a means of reducing the demand.

Legalisation/Decriminalisation.

An increasingly popular remedy to the drug problem which is frequently asserted is that by legalising drug taking in the same way as it is legal to consume alcohol or tobacco under certain defined circumstances the "profits would be taken out of crime". It would be possible to organise official outlets of drugs of defined strength and purity, which could be taxed to provide income to offset any additional burden on the NHS. The "wasted resources" applied to enforcement and the criminal justice system could then be more appropriately used for the benefit of society in general. These are remarkably naïve arguments, which do not bear much examination, but many prominent and intelligent people have been seduced into accepting a patently and demonstrably false logic (see later).

There is no single answer to the World Drug Problem.

Despite the fact that the plague of drug abuse has become a major global problem threatening the fabric of society and which has become deeply rooted everywhere, world leaders do not seem to give it the priority that it demands. It is foolish to imagine that drug trafficking can be eliminated; the aim must be to reduce it to manageable proportions and to reduce demand by education.

There is no magic formula to make drug abuse disappear. Therefore, it seems that it is necessary for a unified effort to be adopted which should be reinforced by sanctions for non-compliance. It is necessary to have international agreements that embrace continued enforcement of anti-drug laws; reduce both supply and demand, provide treatment, recognise appropriate measures of harm reduction/minimisation, and make provision for local needs. Clearly a combined strategy, which builds on international consensus and properly validated methods based on accurate information, must be the way forward. (See concluding chapter).

There must be a shared responsibility amongst governments consisting of a comprehensive, balanced and co-ordinated approach, which recognises and addresses the individual needs of each country. Such programmes must be integrated and should aim at promoting the health and well-being of individuals and preserving the economic stability of countries and world markets. The primary aim must be to reduce the adverse consequences brought about by the illegal drug trade.

There must be a sustained political commitment, which is reinforced by the wealthier and more powerful countries supporting the developing world and recognising the root causes of attitudes and problems. Global organisations must adopt policies which will ensure the reduction of the illicit drug market and must be encouraged to recognise where past failures have, on occasions, unwittingly assisted and promoted the illicit drug trade.

All countries should adopt effective measures at national, regional and international levels against the illicit drug trade and this should be reflected in trade agreements between partner nations so that this priority is paramount in the relationships that are developed between them.

Every international agreement should contain an effective and enforceable commitment to reducing the drug trade and the demand for drugs. Advanced countries must help developing nations to make demand and supply reduction a priority. Where countries see advantage in conniving at or encouraging the drug trade for economic, political, security or strategic reasons, they must be helped to avoid following that path and assisted in every way possible to establish an alternative and drug free approach.

Appendix to Chapter 1: ~

Overview of Narcotics Smuggled along SW Border of the USA: The following is an extract from DEA testimony given by Chief of Operations Richard A Fiano, on 24.9.99 to the Congressional Sub-Committee on Criminal Justice, Drug Policy and Human Resources: -

"With the disruption of the Cali syndicate, Mexican groups such as the Amado Carrillo-Fuentes organization, the Arellano-Felix cartel, the Amezcua-Contreras brothers, and the Caro-Quintero group, consolidated their power and began to dominate drug trafficking along the U.S.-Mexico border and in many U.S. cities. These organisations are no longer simply 'middlemen' in the cocaine transportation business but reach into the very foundations of Mexican society. Events in Mexico and along the border emphasise the fact that trafficking groups from Mexico are now a significant force in international organised crime.

The violence that is an essential part of the operations of these ruthless and powerful organisations impacts upon innocent citizens across the United States. The traffickers' willingness to murder and intimidate witnesses and public officials has allowed them to develop into the present day threat they present to the citizens of the United States and Mexico. Drug traffickers continue their brazen attacks against both U.S. and Mexican law enforcement officials and their sources of information.

Recent intelligence reports indicate that approximately 60% of the cocaine available in the United States crosses over the U.S.-Mexico border. Typically, large cocaine shipments are transported from Colombia, via commercial shipping and "Go-fast" boats and off-loaded in Mexican port cities. The cocaine is transported through Mexico, usually by trucks, where it is warehoused in cities like Guadalajara or Juarez, which are operating bases for the major organisations. Cocaine loads are then driven across the U.S.-Mexican border and taken to major distribution centres within the U.S., such as Los Angeles, Chicago, or Phoenix. Surrogates of the major drug lords wait for instructions, often provided over encrypted communications devices----phones, faxes, pagers or computers---telling them where to warehouse smaller loads, who to contact for transportation services, and who to return the eventual profits to. Individuals sent to the United States from Mexico and who are often here illegally, contract with U.S. trucking establishments to move loads across the country. Once the loads arrive in an area that is close to the eventual terminal point, safe houses are established for workers who watch over the cocaine supplies and arrange for it to be distributed by wholesale dealers within the vicinity. These distributors have traditionally been Colombian nationals or individuals from the Dominican Republic; recently DEA has come upon evidence that Mexican trafficking organisations are directly involved in cocaine distribution in New York City.

We have not only identified the drug lords themselves but also in most cases, the key members of their command and control structure. The combined investigations of DEA, FBI, the U.S. Customs Service and members of state and local police departments have resulted in the seizure of hundreds of tons of drugs, hundreds of millions of dollars in drug proceeds and most importantly, several significant indictments. In fact, some of the leaders of these organisations---Ramon and Benjamin Arellano-Felix, Jesus Amezcua-Contreras, Vicente Carrillo-Fuentes----have become almost household names in every major law enforcement department in the United States. Despite the evidence of the crimes they have committed within the U.S. and the notoriety these traffickers have gained, they have been able continually, to evade arrest and prosecution. The primary reason they have been able to avoid arrest and continue to ship drugs into the United States is attributable to their ability to intimidate witnesses, assassinate, and corrupt public officials.

Methamphetamine trafficking operates in a similar fashion, with major organised crime groups in Mexico obtaining the precursor chemicals necessary for methamphetamine production from sources in other countries, such as China and India, as well as from rogue chemical suppliers in the United States. Super methamphetamine labs, capable of producing hundreds of pounds of methamphetamine on a weekly basis, are established in Mexico or in California, where the methamphetamine is provided to traffickers to distribute across the United States. It is common today to find traffickers from Mexico, most of which are illegal aliens, established in communities like Boise, Des Moines, Omaha, Charlotte and Kansas City, distributing multi-pound quantities of methamphetamine.

The impact of methamphetamine trafficking, from all drug trafficking sources, on U.S. communities has been devastating. In Iowa, health experts have expressed grave concern about the 4000 infants affected by drugs, ninety-percent of which were exposed to methamphetamine. An expert associated with Marshall County Iowa's Juvenile Court Services estimated in 1998 that one-third of the 1,600 students at Marshalltown High School have tried methamphetamine.

Furthermore, there have been numerous incidents where children have been injured or killed by explosions and fires resulting from their parents 'cooking" methamphetamine. In a major DEA case, a working methamphetamine lab established by traffickers from Mexico was discovered in an equestrian center where children were taking riding lessons. In another case investigated by the DEA, an operational methamphetamine lab, capable of producing 180 pounds of methamphetamine, was discovered within a thousand feet of a junior high school.

Heroin from Mexico now represents 14% of the heroin seized in the United States by federal authorities, and it is estimated that organised crime figures in Mexico produced six metric tons of heroin, last year. A current study being conducted by DEA indicates that as much as 29% of the heroin being used in the U.S. is being smuggled in by the Mexico-based organised crime syndicates. Mexican black tar heroin is produced in Mexico, and transported over the border in cars and trucks. Like cocaine and methamphetamine it is trafficked by associates of the organised criminal groups in Mexico, and provided to dealers and users in the Southwest, Northwest, and Midwest areas of the United States. At one time, it was commonplace for couriers to carry two pounds or so of heroin into the United States; recently, quantities of heroin seized from individuals have increased as is evidenced by larger seizures in a number of towns in Texas. This heroin is extremely potent, and its use has resulted in a significant number of deaths. In the small town of Plano, Texas, the dangerously high levels of purity and easy availability resulted in 19 heroin-related deaths and 3 near fatal overdoses since September 1994. Just this past May, former Dallas Cowboy football player Mark Tuanai died of a heroin overdose in Plano. In response to these tragedies, the DEA and Plano Police Department formed a Heroin Task Force to investigate, identify, and prosecute the persons responsible for the importation and distribution of the heroin responsible for these deaths.

Mexican black tar heroin is also common in the Pacific Northwest. Last January, officers from the California Highway Patrol working near Sacramento, stopped a speeding car driven by a sixteen-year-old Mexican national. He, and a passenger, were from Michoacan, Mexico. A search of the car yielded six-kilogram packages of Mexican black tar heroin intended for distribution in Yakima, Washington.

Seattle, Washington has suffered from a dramatic increase in heroin overdose deaths. According to health experts, heroin deaths increased in 1998 to 138. This figure is triple the number of heroin deaths in Seattle during the 1980's. Experts also estimate that there are 20,000 heroin addicts in Seattle and the surrounding area. Traffickers from Mexico use the I-5 highway to bring their product to cities and suburbs in Washington State.

Marijuana from Mexico dominates the illicit U.S. import market. Seizures of Mexican marijuana have increased from 102 metric tons in 1991 to 742 metric tons in 1998. Marijuana organizations from Mexico are very powerful and violent. In some places, traffickers from Mexico have established growing operations within the United States. In a recent case in Idaho, the DEA Boise office, working with other Federal, state and local law enforcement officials, arrested a group of illegal aliens from Zacatecas, Mexico. A total of 114,000 marijuana plants, weighing almost 20 tons, were seized. This operation represented the largest marijuana seizure ever in the state of Idaho.

It is important to note that although many of the transactions relating to the drug trade take place on U.S. soil, the major international organised crime bosses headquartered in Mexico direct the details of their multi-billion dollar business step by step. They are responsible not only for the business decisions being made, but ultimately for the devastation that too many American communities have suffered as a result of the influx of cocaine, methamphetamine, heroin and marijuana."

CHAPTER 2
The Convergence Between Drug Trafficking, Organised Crime And Terrorism.

Drug trafficking has proved to be so profitable that it was inevitable that criminal groups would take advantage of the easy, tax free income to further their own crimes. Whilst it is not intended that this book should be a definitive study of this particular aspect of drugs it is necessary that the connection should be demonstrated because the financial and other crimes associated with drug trafficking have an impact on everyone. There is a need to point up that consuming drugs is not simply a matter of personal choice but that the consequences of relatively small transactions are far-reaching and hugely damaging.

The UN has estimated that drug trafficking represents between 8-10% of global trade. It is facilitated by "globalisation" and the movement of huge amounts of money around the world may be achieved at the "click of a mouse". Small and remote islands have set up 'brass plate' banks, which facilitate money laundering on a vast scale, and make the tracing of criminal assets and the investigation of crimes hugely difficult. It has been estimated that at least $500 billion (approx. 2% of global GDP 2002) is laundered annually and much of this money finds its way into 'legitimate' businesses so that tracing it becomes almost impossible. Increasingly sophisticated encryption techniques make the investigation of electronic crimes more difficult.

In 1998 the United Nations held a special session of the General Assembly on drugs (UNGASS) and in a declaration issued from that meeting it expressed particular concern at the way in which drug trafficking profits were being increasingly used to fund organised crime and acts of terrorism. In the opinion of the then Attorney General of the United States (2004) - John Ashcroft - "Drugs and terrorism go together like rats and bubonic plague". Certainly, there is increasing evidence globally that most terrorist organisations gain some of their funds from either producing and trafficking drugs or 'taxing' other organisations that do so.

International terror groups require significant funds to organise, recruit, train, and equip supporters of their causes. They also need to fund media campaigns, buy political support and win public sympathy by spending money on social projects. At the height of his success the notorious Colombian Drug Lord - Pablo Escobar spent 60% of his massive income in facilitating his business. There is a relationship between traffickers and some terror groups, which benefits both:

> terrorists often control large areas of countries and can use their power to facilitate the needs of drug traffickers; thus the traffickers gain freedom to

operate and protection for which they are able to supply huge amounts of cash to the advantage of the terrorists in purchasing arms and buying support; both terrorists and traffickers are able to corrupt officials who give access to fraudulent documents and confidential information that helps them to avoid detection and capture or which facilitate their trade.

The most horrific terrorist attack took place in the USA on 11th September 2001. It is estimated that the cost of organising those crimes to Al-Q'aeda was less than $500,000 whereas the financial cost to America is thought to have exceeded $135 billion by 2003; by 2004 the estimate had risen to $639 billion. It was Osama bin Laden who is reported to have said "Hit America hard and at its core". It is not entirely clear that the money used to fund the 9/11 attacks was drug related but there is no doubt that some of the money that has been used to facilitate Al-Q'aeda operations came from the profits arising from the production of opium/heroin in Afghanistan.

The United Nations report on drug production in Afghanistan in 2003 concluded that opium crops generated income of $2.3 billion and that al-Q'aeda and the re-emerging Taliban took much of this. There is little sign of abatement in poppy crops and it is likely to be some years before production is reduced by international efforts. Afghanistan is currently producing more than 89% of the world's supply of heroin (INCB Report 2005). A conservative estimate is that terrorist groups took 10% of the Afghan drug profits in 2003 which means that they generated an income of at least $200 million from drug trafficking alone.

The profits are enormous. For example - if we estimate that the street price of drugs to be $100 per gm then a metric ton would yield $100 million and twice that if the drugs were 'cut' with some other substance to bulk them up. In 2003, the National Criminal Intelligence Service (NCIS) estimated that 30 tons of heroin and 40 tons of cocaine enter the UK annually. Subsequently those estimates were increased (this estimate was confirmed in "The UK Threat Assessment of Serious Organised Crime for 2006/7 by The Serious Organised Crime Agency [SOCA]).

Before the attacks in the USA on 9/11, it was usual for law enforcement agencies to regard drug trafficking and terrorism as separate issues. However, it is increasingly difficult to continue to make that distinction and the reality is that major criminal activities including people smuggling and prostitution, money laundering, gambling, the trafficking in arms and drugs have become interconnected and in some cases interdependent. Once criminal monies have been laundered and passed into legitimate businesses, it becomes harder to trace them and seizure of such assets becomes unlikely. Major criminals have employed advances in technology, finance, communications, and transportation in pursuit of profit and political ideologies. A new breed of criminal entrepreneurs has emerged who have developed cyber-crimes and who exploit every legal loophole and operate where laws are lax.

Following the terror attacks in the USA on 9/11 the United Nations passed resolutions 1373 and 1390 urging States to take prescribed actions to combat terrorism and the financing thereof. In October 2001 the USA passed the USA PATRIOT Act (Providing Appropriate Tools Required to Intercept and Obstruct Terrorism) which expanded criminal offences related to terrorism. This Act has a particularly vague definition of terrorism and some have alleged that it runs close to violating the very things that are generally regarded as the bedrock of democracies.

In 2003, the US State Department had classified 14 of its list of 36 designated foreign terrorist organisations as having some connection with drug activities. The term 'narco-terrorism' has been adopted and in the early days the use of terror tactics by the most infamous of Colombian drug traffickers - Pablo Escobar was designed to promote personal and political profit. However, the modern use of this term more correctly relates to terror groups who use drug money to further their causes. Some of the more significant groups are described below although there are many criminal organisations and smaller terror groups that profit from drug money.

South America:

The principal terror groups associated with drugs are based in Colombia, which has been called a narco-terrorist super-state. They are the National Liberation Army (ELN), the Revolutionary Armed Forces of Colombia (FARC) and the United Self-defence Groups of Colombia (AUC). All three groups benefit from the drug trade as well as other crimes of extortion, kidnapping, and robbery. Both ELN and FARC have waged a long war against the Government of Colombia for over forty years and between them, they control 50% of the country. Since 1964, over 200,000 people have been killed and approximately 3000 kidnappings have occurred annually. The AUC defines itself as a paramilitary umbrella organisation of 13 "self-defence" groups supported by local businessmen and communities, which protects itself against the activities of the other two. Paradoxically, it has turned to drug money to supplement its activities, which were originally hostile to drug trafficking.

FARC/ELN obtain 70% of its funds from drug trafficking and it is said that the profit from drugs has superseded their original Marxist ideologies. They are involved with other international terror groups, particularly Al Q'aeda, Hezbollah and the IRA and they have exchanged drugs for arms. Their activities have spilled over into Central America, Mexico, Panama, Ecuador and Venezuela.

(Evidence of Steven W Casteel, Asst Administrator for Intelligence-DEA
before the US Senate Judiciary Committee May 20 2003).

The Tri-Border area between Brazil, Argentina, and Paraguay is the location for two more major narco-terrorist groups whose activities are normally associated with the Middle East. Hezbollah and the Islamic resistance movement known as HAMAS operate extensively in this region and they generate income from a range of organised criminal activities including the production and trafficking in drugs much of which is destined for their organisations in Lebanon.

In Peru, the Sendero Luminoso (Shining Path or SL) is a declining but violent insurgent group that advocates the overthrow of the Government in order to achieve what it describes as "agrarian communism". It is believed that SL gains income by 'taxing' the drug trade.

Southwest Asia.

Mention has been made already of the connection between the heroin/opium production in Afghanistan and the terrorist groups Al-Q'aeda and the Taliban. Many of the other war lords in that country are also involved in the drug trade and gain their financial resources from the poppy crops. Currently at least 89% of the world supply of heroin comes from Afghanistan.

Most of the drugs from Afghanistan go to Russia and Europe and many of them pass through Central Asian Republics that are ill equipped to combat the sophistication of the drug traffickers. A significant radical Islamic movement formed as recently as 1996 and known as the Islamic Movement of Uzbekistan (IMU) is reported by both the Russian and Uzbek governments to be heavily involved in the Central Asian heroin traffic and in many areas it is effectively in control of the trade. The IMU has close ties with Al-Q'aeda and the Taliban, has shared in training camps for terror groups in Afghanistan, and has received funding from both organisations. Although the IMU has the stated aim of introducing sharia law into Uzbekistan it seems more likely that this is a front for financial gain that is used for terror purposes.

(Jane's Intelligence Review and UN sources).

Drugs are produced in Turkey but it is also a significant transit country for heroin from Afghanistan. An active terror group is the Kurdistan Worker's Party (PKK) that was founded in 1974 by Abdullah Ocalan while he was at Ankara University. This group describes itself as a revolutionary socialist organisation and comprises Turkish Kurds whose primary aim is the establishment of an independent Kurdish nation. It was not until the 1990s that the group indulged in acts or urban terrorism and since that time the group has been reported as being responsible for over 30,000 deaths. The PKK is active throughout Europe and has a presence in South Africa and the Turkish government regularly reports that the PKK is deeply involved in the production, processing, and trafficking of heroin. It is asserted that the group is responsible for the production and handling of over 60 tons of heroin annually from which it generates an annual income of $40 million. The group is thought to control a significant part of the European heroin trade and it supplements its income by kidnapping and violent crimes.

There are an increasing number of reports that Russian Organised Crime (the Mafiya) is heavily involved in the drug trade globally. Much of the heroin from Afghanistan fetches up in Russia and the addiction rates there are increasing at an horrific rate. Alliances have been reported with the Italian Mafia, Mexican and Colombian trafficking groups, the Japanese Yakuza, Chinese Triads and Nigerian criminal gangs and there is little doubt that the Russian Organised Crime groups are heavily involved in smuggling drugs into continental USA and Europe. These criminals are also involved in clandestine laboratories for the production of amphetamine type stimulants (ATS) and the transportation of precursor chemicals necessary for the illicit production of drugs globally.

Southeast Asia.

A well-known group often referred to as the Tamil Tigers is the Liberation Tigers of Tamil Eelam (LTTE). Originally sponsored by the Soviet Union this organisation was founded in 1976 when it separated from another group, but it was not until the early 1980s that the LTTE used violence to further its conflict with the government of Sri Lanka. It received terrorist training from the Palestinian Liberation Organisation (PLO). It has a group of suicide bombers known as the Black Tigers and it indulges in political assassinations and bombings. According to the US Drug Enforcement Administration, the group gains its funds from drug trafficking and it is especially noted for supplying couriers who move drugs around Europe. There are also reports that LTTE members have transferred weapons from al-Q'aeda to the Abu Sayyaf group in the Philippines. It is reported that the Tamil Tigers have been responsible for the death of over 65,000 people and the displacement of thousands of other people from their villages and homes.

In 2000, it is alleged that Yassir Arafat approached the Black Tigers to provide suicide bombers for attacks on Israel but there is no published evidence that this occurred.
There are several groups in The Philippines that are reported to be involved in the cultivation, trafficking and distribution of drugs, especially marijuana. The New People's Army (NPA) is the operational wing of the Communist Party of the Philippines dedicated to the overthrow of the government by guerrilla tactics. US sources indicate that this group is actively involved in the drug trafficking/production in order to support their insurgency. It has also been reported that this organisation provides protection for marijuana growers as well as being deeply involved with ATS.

Other groups are The Moro Liberation Front (MNLF) and Moro Islamic Liberation Front (MILF) both of which are Islamic terror groups operating in the South of the Philippines in the Mindanao region. In 1991 because of a rift between activists, the Abu Sayyaf Group emerged. Both MNLF and MILF are involved in drug trafficking and gain their income from this.

The Abu Sayyaf Group is probably the principal terrorist group operating in the Philippines and elsewhere. The US government designates it as a terror group associated with kidnappings, drugs and arms smuggling, extortion and organised crime. All three Philippine groups have links with Al-Q'aeda through Jemaah Islamiya (JI) the group responsible for the Bali bombing in Indonesia.

Myanmar (Burma) is a major producer of both heroin and ATS and although the United Wa State Army in Shan Province is not officially designated as a terror group, nevertheless it is responsible for major drug production and some of the proceeds downstream are used to facilitate terror groups.

Other terrorist organisations which are involved with and profit from the drug trade are ~ the Sicilian Mafia, the IRA, PLO, Hamas, Hezbollah and the Kosovo Protection Corps (formerly the Kosovo Liberation Army). In Canada there are strong links with drugs and organised crime resting with the Hell's Angels gangs

Narco-terrorism is a significant crime but the reality is that almost all organised crime is inter-related. The criminal masterminds will take their profit wherever they can find it, certainly in drug trafficking which is hugely rewarding, but also in racketeering, money laundering, arms smuggling, the gold and diamond markets and the exploitation of those unfortunates who seek asylum and a better life elsewhere. It is also important to remember that certain rogue states sponsor drug trafficking for political reasons and in its report of the International Narcotics Control Scrutiny Report (INCSR) for 2004 the US government indicated its suspicions that North Korea is one of those states.

It has to be remembered that because drug trafficking is so profitable the terror groups associated with the trade use their financial power to undermine the economies of their targets as well as trying to create large numbers of addicts that will cause another drain on their targets. Money laundering is the most common way of using their profits and if this goes unchecked laundering can: ~

- erode the integrity of financial institutions;
- adversely affect currency and interest rates;
- undermine national economies and currency;

- disrupt economic development;
- damage legitimate business;
- threaten national and international security;
- cause global financial crises.

The criminals have multiple choices for their illicit activities and their money is laundered through currency exchanges, stock brokers, banks and insurance companies, precious metal dealers, casinos, auto-dealerships, "time shares" and offshore facilities etc. In December 2000 the UN Convention against Trans-national Organised Crime was signed by 125 countries together with two other protocols against activities linked inextricably with drug-trafficking - trafficking in persons and migrant smuggling.

What should businesses with international interests do?

Since the end of the Cold War there has been a different emphasis on terrorist targeting. Whereas before it was thought that terrorist activities were more likely to be state sponsored now there is an added dimension in that small groups with different ideologies have seen the vulnerability of the super- power and are prepared to attack it economically. For some groups the motivation is religious but for others it is simply to challenge a different and alien culture. Whatever the reason, international corporations are seen as legitimate targets and so it is necessary that they take certain measures to protect their interests and act in ways that are less likely to provoke extreme responses from terrorist groups: ~

- the demonstration of good business ethics and corporate social responsibility are important

- they should avoid giving the impression that they are exploiting a country's natural resources for selfish interests

- they must understand and respect the cultural and natural environment

- be ecologically responsible

- know and respect their employees and introduce appropriate and relevant policies

- not assume that all terrorist groups are organised and highly trained ~ some are opportunists without specific membership of a terrorist organisation

- publish their policies and involve the local communities.

CHAPTER 3
Anti-Drug Strategies.

There are three major conventions of the United Nations aimed a controlling illicit drug trafficking. These conventions are designed to ensure that drugs are available only for legitimate medical and research purposes.

Parties to these conventions are required to take all practicable measures for the prevention of the abuse of narcotic drugs or psychotropic substances. They are also expected to take steps "for the early identification, treatment, education, aftercare, rehabilitation and social reintegration of the persons involved", who may have become dependent upon these substances.

The conventions require that all signatories "shall adopt appropriate measures aimed at eliminating or reducing illicit demand for narcotic drugs and psychotropic substances, with a view to reducing human suffering and eliminating financial incentives for illicit traffic". Such measures include the introduction of legislation to combat money laundering and any other activities, which facilitate the illicit drug trade.

It is interesting to note that the UN Convention on the Rights of the Child emphasises the need particularly to protect children from the abuse of narcotic drugs and psychotropic substances (UN. Convention on the Rights of the Child ,1989 article 33).In 2006 the year was specially designated by UNODC to emphasise the need to protect children from the adverse effects of dangerous drugs.

In 1998, a special session of the United Nations General Assembly (UNGASS) emphasised the need for international opposition to the illicit drug trade and that position was reaffirmed in the mid-term review of that agreement in April 2003. UNGASS recognised that any drug prevention strategy needs to be long-term and a proposal was adopted that member states should prepare a ten year conceptual framework to counter the drug programme.

It was also agreed that five and ten year target dates should be set for reducing the supply and demand for illicit drugs. Target dates were set for member states to act in specified areas. 2003 was established as date for action to be adopted to reduce trafficking in amphetamine-type stimulants, to introduce legislation against money laundering, for the promotion of judicial co-operation, and implementing demand reduction strategies. The year 2008 was set as the date for achieving significant results in demand reduction; eliminating or reducing illicit drug cultivation; and reducing the manufacture and trafficking in psychotropic substances, including synthetic 'designer' drugs and precursor chemicals.

A set of "Guiding Principles on Drug Demand Reduction" was issued to coincide with the special session of the General Assembly and this emphasised the view that demand reduction must be a major factor in the global response to the drug problem.

Most national anti-drug strategies are based on the UN Conventions. These set minimum standards and it is open to participating countries to adopt appropriate laws and policies which best suit their own environment but which also promote international co-operation in the attempt to reduce both supply and demand of these substances. In 2003, the UN renewed its commitment to the Conventions against drugs.

Examination of the Strategy Documents of the USA and the UK gives an idea of the ways in which governments have indicated that they will tackle domestic problems. In the case of the United States, the strategy involves much activity overseas, particularly in Latin America but increasingly in Central Asia both of which export massive quantities of the drugs and many have flooded the American market.

"Plan Colombia", for example, saw vast sums of money devoted to eliminating the production of the coca plant. In Bolivia and Peru, American policies were heavily criticised because of the millions of people whose livelihood depends upon growing the raw material for cocaine, and to a lesser extent, heroin. President Bush's War on Terrorism that included attempts to eliminate the opium poppy in Afghanistan met with little success.

In April 2003 UNODC took part in a mid-term review of progress of UNGASS (United Nations General Assembly Special Session on Drugs) to examine whether the international community was on track to achieve those goals. At that time the global drug situation was assessed as follows: ~

- Drug Abuse – international efforts to reduce the abuse of illicit drugs had shown signs of progress particularly in the case of heroin and cocaine where there were signs of production stabilisation and reduction in some regions. This gave rise to the hope that greater achievements are possible. However, there were worrying signs regarding the production and consumption of synthetic drugs and the consumption of cannabis showed a significant rise. A related health concern is the spread of HIV/AIDS because of injecting drug use in Eastern Europe and the North Pacific Regions. The UN Report on Global Drug Trends 2003 indicated that the emergence of synthetic drugs – amphetamine type stimulants (ATS) including amphetamine, methamphetamine and Ecstasy must be regarded as 'Public Enemy Number One' among illicit drugs.

- Cultivation and Production – the production of coca declined thus reducing the availability of cocaine but the amount produced remains significant. Opium production showed signs of diminishing, particularly in SE Asia; Afghanistan remained the primary producer with evidence of bumper crops that year. Cannabis is grown on every continent to an extent that is hard to establish but abuse is increasing. The output of ATS has spread and high levels are exported from Myanmar.

- Regional differences – a clear pattern shows that opiates are the main drugs of abuse in Europe, Asia and Oceania; cocaine in the Americas (and increasingly in Europe) ATS in East and SE Asia and, to a lesser extent in North America and Europe. Cannabis is consumed everywhere but its most serious effects are felt in Africa.

The mid-term review concluded that the thrust of UN policy on drug control, demand reduction, alternative development and international co-operation was working satisfactorily but that efforts had been hampered by the inadequacy of data. Governments were invited to continue internationally agreed efforts to further build the evidence base for policy development and improvement purposes.

 ## USA – National Drug Control Strategy.

Various strategy documents have promoted a "long-term plan to change American attitudes and behaviour with regard to illegal drugs". They have proposed a reduction of drug use and availability by 50%, which, if achieved would mean that only 3% of the household population over the age of 12 would use illegal drugs. The main points of focus are: -

- Educating children – based on studies that have demonstrated that when children know the dangers of drugs, their rate of drug use drops;

- Decreasing the addicted population – which represents a quarter of all drug users who consume two thirds of all drugs in America;

- Breaking the cycle of drugs and crime – based on studies which have shown that the majority of prisoners committed their crimes to buy drugs or while under their influence;

- Securing US borders – to prevent as many drugs as possible from entering the USA;

- Reducing the supply of drugs – to reduce domestic availability and overseas production.

Overall, the intention behind the strategy is to shrink the American demand for illegal drugs through education, prevention, and treatment, and to attack the supply of drugs through vigorous law enforcement and international co-operation. The documents show clear recognition that if children reach adulthood without using illegal drugs, alcohol and tobacco, they are unlikely to develop a chemical dependency problem in adulthood. That being so, the strategy recognises the need to involve parents, coaches, mentors, teachers, clergy and others as role models and guides in a broad based prevention campaign.

A former Director of the Office of National Drug Control Policy, General Barry McCaffrey, stated - "We are confident that a balanced strategy that relies on prevention, treatment, law enforcement, supply reduction and international co-ordination can dramatically reduce the prevalence and social consequences of drug abuse".

The 2002 document identified three National Priorities: ~

- Stopping Use before it Starts ~ Education and Community Action;

- Healing America's Drug Users ~ Getting Treatment Resources Where They Are Needed;

- Disrupting the Market ~ Attacking the Economic Basis of the Drug Trade.

This document emphasised the need for an honest effort to integrate the identified priorities, implying that there has not been a wholehearted commitment on the part of some people to address a major problem with sufficient funding and resources to make a real and lasting difference. Subsequent Strategy documents endorsed these objectives and that issued in 2006 pointed to a drop in use by young people of methamphetamine, steroids, marijuana, LSD, Ecstasy and some other club drugs. The consumption of tobacco and alcohol had also dropped.

A symbiosis between enforcement, education, and treatment policies was identified as the most effective way forward. Law enforcement is believed not only to attack the major suppliers and dealers, but also it sets a social yardstick against which to measure personal conduct and where that fails, it helps divert users into treatment. Treatment is assisted to become more efficient by the influence, which enforcement provides over the clients served by that system. In return, effective treatment programmes reduce the problem for law enforcement officers by helping to reduce the market for drugs. Accurate and effective education helps to bring about demand reduction, which in turn reduces the market

This combined strategy was designed to diminish the burdens placed on society by illicit drug abuse, but there is the recognition that it is unrealistic to believe that drug abuse will be totally eliminated from society. All that can be hoped for in the short-term is effective management of an enormous problem combined with the political and social need to address the causes that induce people to take drugs. Successive strategy documents followed this philosophy.

An overview of the American Problem.

Statistics and percentages can be both misleading and confusing to the uninitiated, which includes the majority of us. Thus when the figure of 6.4% is given as the percentage of the American population thought to use illegal drugs, it is easy to assume that figure to be not very significant. However, it represents approximately 17 million people (out of a total population of approx. 275 million). Add to that the frightening fact that over 73% of regular drug users are thought to be in employment in the US, and any sensible person has cause to be alarmed.

The strategy documents points out that the figure of 6.4% is significantly lower than the 1979 percentage of 17.5%, but they also acknowledge this to be much too high and state that drug use is a reflection of social attitudes. Unfortunately, in common with the experience in many other countries, young people's attitudes towards substance abuse became more permissive and their perception of drugs as being inherently dangerous diminished for a period, from 1990.

There has been a corresponding increase in the use of illegal drugs among young people. The danger highlighted by that situation is that soon that young generation will become adults who have grown-up having established a pattern of, or a tolerance towards, drug abuse. According to a 1997 survey conducted by the Harvard School of Public Health, drugs were identified as the most serious problem facing children in the United States. The US strategy recognised its main priority as being demand reduction with prevention being the key and therefore the main-focus and primary goal is to educate and enable American youth to reject substance abuse.

Elements of the strategy: -

Democratic – the strategy emphasises the need to protect individual liberty and to respect the rule of law. Internationally the challenge is seen as being able to develop effective, co-operative programmes which respect national sovereignty and reduce the cultivation, production, trafficking, distribution, and use of illegal drugs while supporting democratic governance and human rights;

Outcome–orientated – the strategy must be accountable by providing indicators of performance achievements measurable against targets which gauge progress towards each of the declared goals and objectives;

Comprehensiveness – which requires a multifaceted, balanced, programme attacking both drug supply and demand. No single tactic, pursued alone or to the detriment of other possible and valuable initiatives, can work. Prevention, education, treatment, workplace programmes, research, law enforcement, interdiction, and drug crop reduction must all be components of the strategy;

Long-term – the anti-drug programme requires the education of each new generation and continuous opposition to drug traffickers;

Wide-ranging – the response must support the needs of families, schools, and communities. International aspects of drug control must be addressed through bilateral, regional, and global accords;

Realistic – although drug use cannot be eliminated completely, the approach need not compromise American ideals;

Science-based – a rational policy must be based on accurate, research based information, measured over time by objective performance measurements, and adjusted according to that information.

Goals of the Strategies

- Educate and enable America's youth to reject illegal drugs as well as alcohol and tobacco.

- Increase the safety of America's citizens by substantially reducing drug-related crime and violence.

- Reduce health and social costs to the public of illegal drug use.

- Shield America's land and sea frontiers from the drug threat.

- Break foreign and domestic drug sources of supply.

Without these efforts, the consequences of drug abuse would be much more serious. Accidents, crime, domestic violence, illness, lost opportunities, and reduced productivity, are direct consequences of substance abuse. Drug and alcohol use by children is often associated with other forms of unhealthy, unproductive behaviour, including delinquency and high-risk sexual activity. Young people, whose bodies and minds have not fully matured and developed are said to be particularly vulnerable to the ill effects of drug abuse not only at the time of misuse but also in later years when unforeseen consequences occur.

Whilst the theme of annual Strategy Reports has remained constant it is updated and amended to take account of developing problems. In the report for 2004, special emphasis was placed on the need to confront the illegal diversion and abuse of prescription drugs. The non-medical use of prescription drugs became an increasingly widespread and serious problem in the previous decade, especially the abuse of opioid pain killers and the following information gave rise to concern: ~

- Non-medical use of narcotic pain relievers, tranquillisers, stimulants and sedatives ranked second behind marijuana/cannabis as a category of illicit drug abuse;
- In 2002 6.2 million Americans were abusers of prescription drugs;
- 13.7% of youth 12-17 years had abused these drugs at least once during their lives; and
- Emergency Room visits resulting from narcotic pain reliever's abuse increased 163% from 1995.

Included in the 2004 Strategy was the education of professionals and consumers and an outreach to businesses involved in Internet commerce, pharmaceutical manufacturers, and pharmacies as well as increased investigation and enforcement activities. New programmes included:

- Careful consideration of labelling and the commercial description of opiate drug products;
- Ensuring wider dissemination of education and training on appropriate pain management and opioid treatment procedures for physicians authorised to prescribe controlled substances;
- Increasing the number of prescription monitoring programmes in the hope of identifying abusers and 'doctor shoppers' who seek multiple prescriptions;
- Using web crawler/data mining technology to identify, investigate, and prosecute "pill-mills" - Internet pharmacies that provide substances illegally.

This Strategy was introduced coincidentally with the release of the Annual Report of the International Narcotics Control Board that drew attention to the increase in 'cyber-trafficking' of pharmaceutical products, which it attributed to lax control of the Internet globally. The INCB also drew attention to the "dangerously widespread" perception that the misuse of prescription drugs is not as harmful as the misuse of illegal drugs.

The United Kingdom's Ten Year Strategy for Tackling Drugs Misuse.

This strategy is also based on the belief that dealing with the drug problem requires a continuous and long-term approach, which is informed by accurate and research based information. The supporting vision is for a healthy and confident society with a reducing vulnerability to the harm caused by drugs. There is also an acknowledgement that difficulties with drugs are frequently linked with other social problems, which need to be addressed in tandem with any specific strategies aimed at drug abuse.

A Social Exclusion Unit was given the responsibility for looking at many of the problems that are often associated with drug taking. Research has indicated many reasons why people resort to mind-altering drugs for relief from their problems. It is acknowledged that drugs do not respect social boundaries of colour, class, or creed and that sometimes people use drugs as an experiment or because they anticipate enjoyment and pleasure, particularly in clubs or at social functions. However, the most frequently cited reasons for drug misuse are usually related to low self-esteem, unemployment, and poor prospects of ever obtaining a job, low educational achievement, boredom, and physical, psychological or family problems. Drug misuse can exacerbate some of these problems particularly lack of motivation to lead a useful and positive life (amotivational syndrome).

Many children and young people take drugs because of their immaturity and their inability to resist social pressures. These may be introduced by school friends, personal circumstances, advertising and media representations, the Internet, the ready availability of illicit drugs, and the deliberately false information that is peddled by dealers and those whose interests are served by a successful illicit drug trade.

A key element in the strategy is through the Drug Action Teams (DATs) which have been established in all areas designed to 'ensure a greater cohesion of effort and sharing of resources amongst health and local authorities, criminal justice agencies and other key players'. These teams are required to draw up agreed action plans which are in accordance with the national strategy and to ensure a good prioritisation of local needs in the campaign against drug abuse. The First Annual Report of the UK Anti-Drug Co-ordinator (1999) acknowledged that the DATs were not consistent across the country.

In April 1998, the Government issued its 10-year strategy for tackling drug misuse, which has four main aims: -

- To help young people resist drug misuse in order to achieve their full potential in society;

- To protect our communities from drug related anti-social and criminal behaviour;

- To enable people with drug problems to overcome them and live healthy crime-free lives;

- To stifle the availability of illegal drugs on our streets.

The Underlying Principles of the Strategy.

- **Integration.** Drug problems do not occur in isolation. The connection with other social problems to be addressed by the Social Exclusion Unit looking at associated problems such as school exclusions, truancy, rough sleeping, and poor housing. The Government claims to be addressing inequalities by a large programme to get people off benefits and into work and a series of reforms in the welfare state, education, health, criminal justice, and the economy.

- **Evidence.** The strategy has to be based on accurate, independent research approached analytically.

- **Joint Action.** - has a far greater impact on the complex drugs problem than disparate activity.

- **Consistency of Action.** Drugs misuse is a national problem requiring a consistent, equitable approach.

- **Effective Communication.** Clear, consistent messages reinforcing the point that drug taking can be harmful.

- **Accountability.** Through the Co-ordinator's Annual Report and Plan of Action, an objective assessment of both performance and achievement to be made.

An overview of the UK Drug Problem: -

The British experience of drug related problems is very similar to that of any other developed country and although it does not equate with the scale of that described for the USA it is probably the worst in Europe. Nevertheless, there is a significant connection between drugs and crime and the drain on the country's resources are similar with an estimated and rising expenditure in excess of £4 billion in annual costs to the tax-payer because of serious drug abusers (1998 estimate). There is too, much hidden expenditure within other budgets not least of which has shown up within the costs to the police and National Health Service.

Only a small percentage of the population has used drugs (in 2005 thought to be 11.5%), and many of those who have were experimenters or casual users. It has been estimated that there are up to 250,000 people in the UK (out of an estimated population of 59 million) who may be classified as heroin addicts. Many of these people are believed to be responsible for a substantial amount of the drug-related crime and make disproportionate demands on a range of community service agencies including law enforcement, medical and social work.

The strategy document acknowledges that the response to this problem has been far from satisfactory. It recognises that good work is being done but that there are far too many inconsistencies within the operation of the criminal justice system; inadequate treatment and prescribing facilities; haphazard funding arrangements with a bias to reaction rather than prevention.

Added to this there is an inadequacy of accurate, timely and consistent information. Many doctors feel ill-prepared to deal with the problem, there are too few treatment and residential centres, the delay between referral for treatment and actually receiving it is inordinately long and there is not a consistent approach to education within the schools. The Report of the House of Commons Home Affairs Select Committee on drug policy in 2002 drew attention to the lack of a satisfactory approach to education against drug use in many schools. The report emphasised the need for all education programmes to be based on stressing that all drug abuse is harmful and should be resisted.

In other words, it is acknowledged that there is fragmentation and dissipation of effort and resources, lack of adequate training and guidance, and insufficient investment for any system to be able to make the kind of impact on the problem which has been acknowledged as being necessary.

The evidence available in 1998 when the strategy was formulated suggested: -

- Between 2-3% of 11-12 year old schoolchildren have ever taken an illegal drug;

- 23% of pupils aged 14-15 had taken an illegal drug in the last year; 13% in the last month;

- 29% of young people 16-24 had taken within the last year, 14% in the last month;

- Illegal drug use peaks between 16-24 years;

- The age of first use is reducing;

- Cannabis is the most widely used drug;

- Concern that heroin and cocaine use was increasing.

Research by Exeter University published in March 2000 claimed to show that drug use amongst those under 16 had fallen for the third consecutive year and that there had been a levelling off and possibly a downturn in this age group's experience of drugs. Responses from more than 40,000 children aged between 12-15 years in 1999 also suggested that few would change their habits if cannabis were to be legalised. Only 3% of those who had never tried the drug said that they would do so if the drug were legal, 29% said they did not know what their reaction to legalisation would be. Cannabis was by far the most commonly used drug with 19% of 14 & 15 years olds admitting to trying it in 1999. Only 5% had tried amphetamines or solvents (The Times 6.3.00).

The first annual report of the UK Anti-Drug Co-ordinator (1999) referred to "this cycle of despair" which afflicts many communities (cf. "The cycle of deprivation" mentioned by Sir Keith Joseph, Secretary of State for Education in 1968).

One of the major factors in this cycle is the relationship between drugs and crime, which was estimated to be: -

- Approx. 32% of the proceeds of offenders' acquisitive crimes is used to purchase heroin and/or 'crack' cocaine.

- Approx. half of those arrested who reported drug use within the past 12 months believed their drug use and crimes were connected.

- Approx. 30% of those arrested reported current dependence on one or more drugs, and I in 5 had received some kind of treatment with a similar proportion wishing to receive treatment.

- The National Treatment Outcome Research Study (one year follow up) showed reduction in criminal behaviour after treatment of 1/3 amongst residential clients and amongst community methadone clients. The overall reduction in specific offences = approx. 70%.

Many police forces in the UK were reporting a link between drugs and reported crime between 50-70%.

In the case of treatment, the report states that the supply of effective treatment services is failing to match demand and that 'the scope, accessibility and sometimes the effectiveness of available treatments are inconsistent and generally insufficient'. Many of the dependent drug users estimated to be as many as 250,000 people are either failing to seek or failing to receive effective service and under-funding has meant the actual loss of some residential places.

In some prisons, effective drug treatment is available. However, continued success can be frustrated by lack of support when a prisoner is released in circumstances where there is no continuity of support – "… if a person returns to the same problems and the environment that he came from, the likelihood of reverting to his previous drug use is high".

A National Treatment Agency was established in 2001 but the early stages of development indicated that it had some major problems to overcome.

In May 2005 a report from the Home Office indicated the following: ~ More than three-quarters of a million people in England and Wales admitted using the Class A drug in the previous year, making it the second most popular illegal drug after cannabis. Overall, 2.4 percent of the population had used the drug in the past year, compared with 0.6 percent in 1996. The British Crime Survey 2003-4 indicated some 4.9 percent of 16 to 24-year-olds said they had used cocaine in the past year. But the drug's use grew fastest among 25 to 34-year-olds: 4.5 per cent of this age group said they had taken cocaine in the previous year, up from 1.9 per cent in 2003-4. The survey, based on interviews with, 422 people, showed that cocaine users were more likely to be semi-skilled or skilled manual workers than professionals. However, cocaine users were more likely to have degrees or A-levels than no qualifications. More than a million people used Class A drugs, with half a million of them doing so regularly. Nearly a quarter of 16 to 24-year-olds admitted to using Class A drugs more than once a month.

(The Times 27.05.05)

The statistical bulletin on drugs issued from the Home Office in October 2005 indicated the extent of drug use among 16-59 year olds in England and Wales since 1998 when the Government's anti-drug strategy was introduced; it showed that 11 million people had admitted to having taken drugs. The report also showed that use of 'Any drug' among 16-24 year olds had decreased and that Class A use remained stable since 1998. For the 16 to 59 year old age group the use of 'Any drug remained stable and Class A use increased but this was interpreted as being due to a significant increase in cocaine use between 1998 and 2000. The report asserted that since 2000 Class A use remained stable and that the use of both cocaine and cannabis in this age group actually declined.

UK Targets for 2005 and 2008 and the National Plan for 1999/2000.

In accordance with the special session of the UN General Assembly in 1998, the UK set targets for reducing all drugs available in the UK substantially. The most dangerous drugs, which include heroin and cocaine, were specifically mentioned because of the high cost, estimated at between £10-20,000 p.a., of maintaining a habit. Those who are dependent upon these particular drugs are said to be responsible for a substantial proportion of all crime, but particularly theft and housebreaking. The target set for reducing the use of these drugs by people under the age of 25 was 25% within 5 years and 50% within 10 years.

The need for better and shared information systems was recognised. The targets were linked to the strategy document and, in accordance with its aims and objectives, the declared intention was that across the UK: -

Young People - to reduce the proportion of people under 25 reporting use of illegal drugs in the last month and previous year substantially, and to reduce the proportion of young people using the drugs which cause the greatest harm – heroin and cocaine, by 25% by 2005 and – by 50% by 2008.

Communities – the key, performance target is - to reduce levels of repeat offending amongst drug misusing offenders by 25% by 2005 and by 50% by 2008.

Treatment – the key performance target is to increase the participation of problem drug misusers, including prisoners, in drug treatment programmes which have a positive impact on health and crime by 100% by 2008 and by 66% by 2005.

In June 2000, in furtherance of this aim, the Home Secretary announced that he intended setting up a National Treatment Agency in conjunction with the Department of Health. The stated intention was that this new agency would set targets for treatment in all areas, would measure performance outcomes and would co-ordinate activities to ensure best value for money. It remains to be seen how successful this venture may be but it is certain that in the early stages, not all those in need of treatment are receiving it and even if they do, there is no guarantee that it will be either adequate or totally effective.

Availability – to reduce access to all drugs amongst young people (under 25) significantly, and to reduce access to the drugs which cause the greatest harm, particularly heroin and cocaine, by 50% by 2008 and by 25% by 2005. This last target necessarily involves a threat assessment and action involving international liaison and the attempt, by a variety of means, to reduce the amount of drugs from entering the country.

The House of Commons Select Committee on Home Affairs reviewed the Government anti drug policy and issued a report in May 2002. At best, this Inquiry may be described as a sampling of opinion rather than a thorough investigation into validated research based on scientific principles.

Of course, views differ but public opinion is ultimately worthless unless it is formed from accurate information and experience. Such views must then be tested rigorously. Public policy should not be based on "street cred" and the results of a low-turn out at elections. Public feeling must be used as a guide to debate not necessarily a justification for change. Similarly, the Government would be unwise to make significant changes in drug policy without an exhaustive examination of all available evidence and the Home Affairs Committee could not claim that it had undertaken that comprehensive task.

The main thrust of the report's recommendations was a move away from what it saw as the emphasis on enforcement. It demonstrated a more liberal approach based on the view that although the majority of young people never acquire a drugs habit, for those who do it is usually a "passing phase" which they will grow out of and which rarely results in long-term harm.

How the members arrived at this conclusion is a mystery considering that most informed opinion is in favour of further research, particularly into the effects of cannabis, Ecstasy, and Amphetamine Type Stimulants. The Committee stated that illicit drug use should never be condoned but it was guilty of the very thing that it criticised, namely, the sending of confusing and "mixed messages".

An influencing equation that seemed to appear in the report was that of 'drugs and death' instead of the long-term harm to individuals and society. Although there is an emphasis on Harm Reduction, it was without the realisation that internationally, this term has been usurped by those who seek to legalise drugs and has become a code for the promotion of drug use. The emphasis must surely be on both demand and supply reduction with treatment where necessary. The Annual Report for 2003 of the International Narcotics Control Board (INCB) re-emphasised that "Harm Reduction" approaches should not be seen to condone or promote drug abuse but should be seen to contribute to a reduction in the abuse of drugs.

Quite properly, the emphasis in all drug-related activity must be the prevention of harm to the individual and society. However, the Committee failed to recognise that placing undue emphasis on Harm Reduction condemns society to a constant cycle of attempting to address the extent of harm that illicit drug use causes. Harm Reduction policies can and do result in a "Ripple Effect" similar to the small pebble thrown into a pond. The circle of influence gets larger and more extensive.

Those opposed to illicit drug use want a policy based on the three strands of thorough public health education, appropriate enforcement and readily available treatment for people unfortunate enough to become dependent on drugs. This is implicit in existing policy but the lack of availability of resources and trained personnel has meant that the drug problem has grown disproportionately. The present Government strategy is incomplete, under-resourced, and lacks credibility.

Although the Committee endorsed "shock treatment" in appropriate cases the 'Just Say No' campaign which was hugely successful in the USA and elsewhere before complacency set in, was largely and wrongly, discredited.

After the publication of the Select Committee Report on Government anti-drug policy, the Home Secretary announced that he would be issuing an updated strategy document later in the year. The UK Government Anti-Drug Co-ordinator announced his resignation in protest over the policy and stated that the Home Secretary had consistently failed to acknowledge that a cogent strategy was already in place and predicted that the new document would be a re-hash of the existing strategy. He accused the Home Secretary of indulging in political "spin" for the sake of appearances.

Updated Drug Strategy 2002.

This strategy set out a range of policies and interventions concentrating on what the Government believed to be the most dangerous drugs, the most damaged communities, and the individuals whose addiction and chaotic lifestyles are most harmful. The document stressed that the Government has no intention of legalising any illicit drug.

The document stated that it was estimated that around 4 million people use at least one illicit drug each year and around 1 million people use at least one of the most dangerous drugs (ecstasy, heroin, and cocaine). The number of problematic users was estimated to be 250,000 and drug misuse costs were estimated in social and economic terms to be between £10-18 billion p.a. It was also estimated that 75% of offenders have misused drugs and arrestees who use heroin and/or cocaine commit almost ten times as many offences as arrestees who do not use drugs.

Key points in the updated strategy are: -

- Preventing today's young people becoming tomorrow's problematic drug users
- Reducing the supply of illegal drugs
- Reducing drug related crime and its impact upon communities
- Reducing drug use and drug-related offending through treatment and support
- Reducing drug-related death through harm minimisation

CHAPTER 4
An examination of some of the issues.
The case made by advocates of the legalisation of drugs.

For more years than most people realise drugs have become a part of everyday life particularly for young people. It is only relatively recently in the U.K. that the enormity of the problem has been realised, and with that realisation has come the assertion that the only way to deal with such a massive global problem is to accept it and to regulate it in ways other than prohibition.

In simple terms, the proposal is that the "War on Drugs" is not only an inappropriate way to deal with drugs, it has become a very costly and demonstrable failure. Vast resources have been poured into the prevention of drug use and the suppression of illicit manufacturing, trafficking, and supply. What is said to be essentially a chronic medical problem has been turned into a criminal justice problem with inappropriate remedies that make "innocent" people criminals. In short, the prohibition monies have been wasted and the vast financial resources applied to this activity would be better spent in other ways for the general benefit of the community.

Indeed, it has been suggested that international drug control activities actually may have worsened the problem at the expense of the health and wellbeing of the nations involved. What are said to be the root causes of the problem are pointed to and it is claimed that by addressing them – unemployment, poverty, poor education, a sense of hopelessness and having nothing to relieve boredom and frustration – not nearly so many people would turn to "mind-altering" substances.

Various pressure groups around the world have mounted campaigns for the legalisation of drugs. Many have argued in good faith that by applying a modified form of control rather than outright de-regulation it would be possible to put the criminals out of business by denying them their profits. At the same time it would be possible to establish a legal regime, which would ensure quality and availability of drugs at affordable prices such that it would not be necessary to commit crime in order to acquire the means to afford them. At a single stroke, so the argument goes, crime would be eliminated, controlled use would be achieved and it would be possible to consider some form of taxation in the same way as for tobacco and alcohol, which could be applied to the treatment of those who needed it. An additional benefit would be that wasted criminal justice resources could be applied elsewhere and more beneficially.

Of course, there are others who argue for legalisation because they assert a personal freedom to use substances in private so long as no harm is done to anyone else. Others put forward a civil rights argument that points out that millions of people take advantage of the legal right to use their drug of choice (alcohol or tobacco) while others are denied legal access to cannabis and other drugs, and punished by draconian sanctions if they break the law. To some this appears to be unconstitutional and manifestly unfair.

Some people, who regard themselves as realists, claim that because the prohibition against illicit drugs has failed, and is not capable of full enforcement, we should accept the world as it has become and adopt a fall back position. Society should learn to live with drugs as an existing problem that is unlikely to go away. A common assertion is that "Prohibition" of alcohol consumption in the United States between the years1920–1934 did not work, so why should it be thought that the prohibition against drugs would be any more successful?" Paradoxically, both advocates for prohibition and legalisation of drugs use this experience in America as a justification for their arguments.

Frequently the pro-legalisation lobby refers to other countries which have legalised or tolerated drugs for personal use. In particular, the "cannabis cafes" in Holland are held up as a policy, which is said to have been extremely successful. The apparently liberal attitude of some Swiss towards heroin use is also claimed as justification for either toleration or legalisation but the full facts and circumstances seldom are described accurately (see later).

A distinction is sometimes made between so-called "soft" or 'recreational' drugs such as cannabis and ecstasy, and the "hard" drugs like heroin and cocaine, which are generally regarded as more harmful and addictive. Any suggestion that "soft" drugs are a "gateway" or stepping-stones to harder substances is denied, as is the notion that they are addictive or inherently harmful.

A concept of "harm reduction" (see later) has grown up around the legalisation or toleration of "soft" drugs which has persuaded some that allowing small consumption and possession on a personal basis is less harmful than grouping all drugs as a class of "forbidden fruit". It is argued that by tolerating the use of cannabis for example, there is no attraction to try harder substances and in many cases the use of a permitted substance will become "boring" and the activity will cease with the passage of time once the initial attraction subsides.

Another peripheral argument sometimes made in favour of the permitted use of cannabis is that this substance is bulky to transport and is not so easily concealed as the more addictive and potent drugs that can be smuggled by individual couriers. One person can transport hugely valuable consignments of addictive substances in powdered form by, for example, swallowing many sealed condoms containing the illicit substance.

It is alleged that this prohibition of a bulky product has encouraged the smuggling and use of a more potent, addictive and harmful drug, which is injected to gain maximum satisfaction and complete use of the substance. Hence, it is said that intravenous use and abuse of heroin and cocaine world wide has been encouraged by prohibition. With the drop in price and ready availability of these substances even young children are turning directly to that which was once the indulgence of only the very wealthy. It is worth noting that the use and transportation of cannabis has increased regardless of the trend towards the harder drugs.

A very attractive argument that is made for the legal use of cannabis is based on the therapeutic and medicinal properties of cannabinoids which are wrongly attributed to the smoking of a joint of cannabis. Anecdotal evidence of the efficacy of treatment and pain relief attributed to cannabis/marijuana is offered. Many have claimed benefits in the treatment of such things as ~ glaucoma, the relief of the nauseating effects of chemotherapy for cancer patients, benefits for sufferers of multiple sclerosis, and the wasting effects of HIV/AIDS. This has been tendered in support of legalisation. For humanitarian reasons the advocates say the law should not turn patients into criminals.

(see later for details on the use of cannabis).

There is too the claim that prohibiting a drug (cannabis) that is so widely and freely used by so many is to encourage disrespect not only for that particular prohibition, but also, for the drugs law in general. This in turn creates a disbelief in, and a devaluation of, all other anti-drug messages and is therefore, counter productive and wasteful of resources.

A further point made in support of legalisation is that the actual harm caused by drugs in terms of deaths and adverse health effects are significantly less than that caused by the "legal" drugs of alcohol and tobacco. In some respects this is valid as it has been claimed that deaths in the U.K. from tobacco use are greater than the sum total of all other non-natural causes of death. It has been estimated that globally there are 20 million deaths in each generation from smoking related illnesses.

Certainly, the costs to the health authorities of smoking and alcohol related illnesses are enormous. In the case of smoking the health related problems are very significant. The danger to health is reinforced by the publishing of government warnings on cigarette packets, and the prohibition of some forms of advertising for tobacco products.

The pro-legalisation advocates concede that such a measure would result in increased use of drugs in the short term but they assert that such initial use would level out to an acceptable and moderate standard in due course.

The total case for legalisation seems to be based upon a conglomeration of assertions that amount to the belief that society's assault on civil liberties has been disastrously and expensively ineffective and counter productive. In short, prohibition produces more costs than benefits and therefore the use of drugs on a personal basis should be permitted. Legalisation would eliminate the expenditure incurred in prohibition; would take the profit out of crime for the criminal suppliers and dealers; would decriminalise understandable human behaviour and thus would prevent the overburdening of a criminal justice system that is manifestly failing to cope. The police would not waste their time on relatively trivial drug offences such as possession of small amounts of cannabis for personal use. The courts would be freed from the backlog of trivial cases. The prisons would not be used as warehouses for drug users who are able to compound their habit in jail and are likely to continue their drug use on release.

Prohibition is said to generate all of the adverse consequences for society associated with crime and violence. Whichever line of justification for legalisation is used, the end-result is claimed to be significantly more realistic, beneficial and cost effective than the policy of a "war on drugs" which can never be won.

Summary of pro-legalisation arguments

- The "war on drugs" has been lost and society should not continue to waste resources in pursuit of failed prohibition policies.

- The wasted resources could and should be used for the betterment of society.

- A legal regime of limited drug use would ensure availability of drugs of the right quality, quantity and at the right price.

- Tax revenues raised from legal drugs could offset any expenditure on associated health problems, as alleged in the case of alcohol and tobacco.

- The criminal law should not be used to inhibit personal freedom to use the drug of choice in private and personal circumstances that cause no harm to others.

- The removal of profits from the drug trade would put suppliers and dealers out of business and thus end crime associated with suppliers and dealers.

- "Soft" or recreational drugs are not a "gateway" to other drugs and should be permitted as in Holland.

- The actual harm in the form of deaths and related health problems is less than that caused by other "legal" drugs – alcohol and tobacco.

- Prohibition of widely used substances such as cannabis and ecstasy encourages disrespect for that law and the anti-drugs messages.

- The medicinal and therapeutic benefits of cannabis are a justification for its legalisation.
- "Prohibition" of alcohol in the USA did not work.
- Substances that are said to cause extreme harm should not be solely in the control of criminals whose only interest is profit.

The case for prohibition:

There has been recognition by the International community that drugs are an enormous global problem. The impact of the illicit drug trade has been huge. It has had such damaging consequences in economic, social, health and welfare terms, that there has been international agreement, and an acceptance of a collective responsibility, that co-operation and a common approach is the only way in which it is possible to address the problem.

There have been three drug control Conventions under the auspices of the United Nations, with the aims of ensuring adequate supplies of narcotic and psychotropic drugs for medical and research purposes only and the prevention of drug abuse to suppress illicit manufacture, diversion and trafficking. There is a broad consensus under international law but inevitably, the weakness lies in the need for compromise between nations with widely differing, cultural, historical, economic and legal traditions. International agreement is difficult to achieve and Conventions are not easily altered once they have been established.

The illicit drug trade moves and adapts to changing circumstances much more rapidly than international agreements, although international co-operation between the various law enforcement agencies has improved significantly in recent times.

According to the United Nations' "World Drug Report" (1997), the guiding principles of the Conventions rest on the control of supply, and that of demand through supply/demand reduction which is normally left for individual countries to address through national legislation. Other appropriate measures in accordance with the perceived problem and local circumstances should be introduced by individual countries but should be made known internationally.

An additional reason for international collaboration has been the need to protect the health and well-being of countries from the spread of communicable diseases such as AIDS/HIV+ which has been exacerbated by the sharing of needles and drugs paraphernalia, and unprotected sexual intercourse. This world problem has required a world response not only in terms of health measures associated with illicit drug control but also in ensuring that education and training are shared in the most beneficial ways that will protect communities.

Any failures in a common approach to a problem such as drugs would result in a complete breakdown in effectiveness. Differing and fragmented responses to a common problem are unacceptable for the wellbeing of the international community and it is therefore, incumbent on national governments to secure the greatest good for the greatest number.

The UN's principal, drug control agency (UNODC-United Nations Office of Drugs and Crime formerly UNDCP and briefly - UNODCCP) has an additional obligation, to consider all criticisms made of the Conventions and to evaluate alternative proposals. To a certain extent this relieves individual states from duplicating that activity by "raising the debate" locally, which is frequently advocated by those in favour of legalisation. The UNODC is a useful forum in which international aspects of the drug issue are constantly under review and this body can consider the global consequences of alternative drug control measures by examining economic, health and social impact assessments.

Despite the assertion that the criminal justice system has failed to bring about "demand reduction", and the elimination of drug abuse, nevertheless, there have been some significant successes in the interdiction of international criminal gangs and a reduction in the number of people who use drugs in some countries. The supporters of prohibition raise the question as to how bad things would have been without the resistance to the illicit drug trade and point to the fact that the majority of people do not wish to consider the legalisation of drugs.

Those in favour of the status quo have noted that the abuse of drugs in several industrialised, western countries appears to have stabilised and may even be on the decline. It is said that legalisation could stimulate both interest and demand and so much of the good that has been achieved already, would be undone. Aggressive and consistent law enforcement combined with education had a very positive effect in the United States in the decade 1985-1995, when the numbers of people admitting to drug use in that period fell by 50%. The number of regular, illegal drug users reduced from 26 million to 13.3 million.

There has been a polarisation of the arguments for and against legalisation, reducing the debate to an "either/or" situation. There is no single answer to the problem and an integrated and co-operative effort is needed. Equally it has been recognised by people on both sides of the divide that a whole range of measures from enforcement to education, from "harm reduction" to the treatment of those who have become dependent, is necessary whatever stance is eventually taken. Even those in favour of legalisation do not appear to favour total de-regulation for all drugs. It is recognised that success is a long-term goal that cannot be achieved without continuous and united efforts; any deviation from the common plan will minimise the probability of success.

The majority opposed to legalisation point out that merely because society erred in permitting the use of two major addictive substances (tobacco and alcohol), that is no reason to introduce a third addictive and costly blight on society. There is recognition that it is extremely unlikely that alcohol and tobacco would have been legalised if their adverse consequences had been foreseen.

Researchers in the USA have demonstrated the devastating increase in dependency that would result from the legalisation of a drug like heroin. They have predicted that far from the initial upsurge in use after de-regulation declining there would be a "capture rate" the same as for cigarettes, i.e. over 50% of new users, would become dependent. They point out that nobody can be sure what the increased amount of dependency on de-regulated drugs would be, but it is an intelligent assumption that there would be a significant rise in the number of addicts. That being likely, it is illogical to support the legalisation of an inherently harmful substance. The cumulative effects of prohibition and interdiction combined with education and treatment have had such a significant impact in stemming the world drug problem so far that it would be unwise to "change horses in mid-stream" (UN World Drug Report 1997).

Those opposed to legalisation point to the huge bureaucracy that would develop as a consequence of any de-regulation. However the newly legalised drugs were controlled, either by central government or by private franchise, the amount of national and international administration would be enormous. It would be necessary to ensure the quality control and the adequacy of supplies and it would be necessary to provide answers to such questions as those posed by the US Drug Enforcement Administration: -

- Should all drugs be legalised?
- To which age groups and types of people should they be available?
- Can anyone regardless of age and mental condition purchase drugs?
- Who will dispense the drugs and do they need to be prescribed?
- Who will pay the costs to society of increased drug use – e.g. health and treatment costs?
- Who will be liable for the damages associated with drug use?

- How should we deal with absenteeism and loss of productivity to businesses?

- How will society pay for increased social costs through dysfunctional families, addictions, and child and domestic abuse?

- How will the revenues from drug sales be taxed and audited?

These and many other issues would have to be addressed. Those in favour of prohibition point to the huge increase in administrative costs alone not to mention the increased drain on the health services that would accrue to society as a result of any de-regulation of an inherently addictive and "mind-altering" substance.

They add that crime will not disappear and the on-costs for the criminal justice system are unlikely to diminish. It is nonsense to pretend that by legalising drugs it would be possible to eradicate the enormously successful, criminal enterprises that account for at least 8% of world trade (UN World Drug Report 1997). Equally it is foolish to pretend that individual and private drug taking imposes no harm on society. It is necessary only to compare the damage that alcohol and tobacco can cause to others with the dangers of "passive smoking", for example and the consequences of people acting under the influence of alcohol.

These issues pose the further question as to - "Why should ordinary citizens assume the costs of self induced harm to those who wish to use addictive and harmful substances?" It is believed that the greater availability of drugs would result in increased use, and legalisation of all or some drugs would not bring any compensating benefits.

A very powerful argument against legalisation is the continuing uncertainty surrounding the long-term effects of some of the so-called, "soft drugs". Supporters of the status quo point to the fact that it took many years before a positive link between smoking and lung cancer was established. In the case of cannabis and ecstasy, for example, similar scientific research and analysis has not been carried out over sufficiently long periods for anyone to be able to say with any certainty, what the effects of using the various substances would be. However, there are strong indications of the potential for great, long-term damage to users. Even in the case of the proposed use of medicinal use of cannabis, the American Institute of Medicine has concluded that there would never be a justification on medical grounds for smoking cannabis. (See section on Cannabis) Any proposed medicinal treatment related to cannabis extracts should be under strict prescription and supervision and the substance should be taken in forms other than smoking.

Normal drugs are required to go through a prolonged period of scientific testing followed by certification and licensing before they can be released for over the counter sales or prescribed by doctors. In the case of untested and unlicensed drugs the question has to be answered as to how they could be marketed and with what sort of health warning. Apart from the legal liability issues for any harm caused, prohibitionists argue that it would be irresponsible for any government to approve any substance about which so little is known.

There is sufficient information available to give rise to the presumption that both cannabis and ecstasy can both be seriously harmful and addictive and there is much evidence to support the theory that they are both "gateway" drugs to other more addictive and harmful substances. Recent research in Australia has reinforced the view that cannabis is an addictive substance (1999 National Alcohol and Drug Addiction Centre (NDARC) Report by – Dr Jennifer Swift). Unfortunately, the force of this argument is often trivialised by the widespread use of both substances and the equally widespread ignorance, which generates disrespect for the anti-drug message. It is also important to emphasise that drug dealers peddle false information about drugs and their effects to promote their trade. Those who favour de-regulation are not prepared to wait for the proper procedures to be followed and many are convinced, particularly in the case of cannabis and ecstasy that the benefits claimed by many current users, outweigh any risks. However, there is a great difference between feeling good after using a substance and actually improving a condition by its use. Many products may result in the user feeling good, without there being any curative effect.

The whole concept of legalising drugs gives rise to all kinds of difficulties. Apart from the questions raised above, if the newly legalised substances were allowed to form part of the free market in the same way as alcohol and tobacco, then with that freedom would follow all of the marketing techniques designed to promote sales and a wider use of the substances. Drugs would be represented as essential fashion accessories to young and impressionable people who would be convinced that if they are "legal", they are not likely to be very harmful. A successful marketing campaign would result in more addictions with associated costs to the health systems and greater social harm than under the prohibition regime.

Legalising the availability of mind altering substances with no guarantee that this would achieve what the advocates claim is seen to be too high-risk a strategy. Prohibitionists point to examples of shortages, including the restrictions on alcohol during the Prohibition era in the United States, where addiction levels had fallen only to rise again once supplies resumed their former levels. They claim that the ready availability of an addictive substance undermines the willpower of someone who is trying to control consumption.

Even if some form of government control were to be applied to the legalised substance by way of taxation, as in the case of tobacco and alcohol products, great care would be necessary. If taxation were too severe, this would encourage a black market designed to circumvent the controls. Organised crime would continue to find ways of maintaining its trade regardless of the legality of the product because no government would give carte-blanche approval for the use of a dangerous substance by all members of society. Any restrictions would give rise to the opportunity for criminal exploitation particularly of the young and vulnerable members of society.

On the subject of tax revenues, prohibitionists believe that they have demonstrated the falsity of the argument that revenues from the taxation of newly legalised substances, together with the "savings" achievable within the criminal justice system, would offset substantially, any additional health costs incurred as a result of new addictions.

The current income from alcohol and tobacco products comes nowhere near covering the direct health care costs involved, not to mention the additional social security costs for victims of cancer, associated heart disease, and the victims of road traffic accidents who are unable to work. No evaluation is possible of the hidden costs that arise from reduced or lost productivity or from sub-standard work, by an employee failing to achieve optimum performance levels because of the effects of drugs. Additionally, those opposed to legalisation point to the costs associated with dysfunctional families, marital breakdown, and child abuse/neglect, physical and mental defects in children born to mothers who are users/abusers, which can have a lifetime impact on the new-born children and in care costs for society.

Those who oppose legalisation reiterate the observation that it is nonsense to pretend that private and personal use of a mind-altering substance does not have an impact upon, and cause harm to others. We pay for irresponsible use of substances through taxation, enhanced risks for society and the associated disruption of our lives because of massive criminal conduct which is so profitable that the manipulators have the power to damage the economies and the wellbeing of whole countries and world regions.
The assertion that legalisation is the better of two evils is also thought to be a flawed argument. Once Pandora's Box has been opened it would be extremely difficult to close it again. Legalisation sends the message of approval – that drugs are acceptable, and the impact that demand reduction by way of education has would be irretrievably damaged at a stroke. In short, those opposed to any form of de-regulation, and who represent the majority of people, argue that legalisation would increase the risks to individuals, families and communities and to world regions, without any acceptable, compensating benefits. Legalisation would be likely to: -

- Convince people that any legal activity cannot be very harmful;
- Increase the availability of all drugs for all people;
- Increase the harmful consequences associated with drugs; and
- Remove the social sanctions normally supported by the legal system.

Any failure to address the significant and seriously debilitating problem is detrimental to society generally. Everyone should accept the responsibility for resisting the acceptance of yet another addictive blight on our societies.

As part of its campaign against drugs the Drug Enforcement Administration in the United States drew up ten major claims that can be made against legalisation: -

- Crime, violence and drug use go hand-in-hand;
- Progress has been made in demand reduction and now is not the time to stop;
- Legalisation will increase use and addiction levels;
- Tax revenues raised would be offset by increased social costs;
- There are no compelling medical reasons for the prescription of cannabis or heroin;
- Legalisation and decriminalisation have failed elsewhere;
- Alcohol has caused significant problems and drugs would make matters worse;
- Compared to the overall budget, drug control spending is minuscule
- Drug prohibition is working;
- Drug legalisation would have adverse effects on low-income families.

The last point raises an interesting factor that is seldom considered by either of the parties in the debate. That is the impact that sudden changes in the status quo would have on those who have become dependent, through no fault of their own, on the world drug trade in botanical based drugs.

The UN reports that the world is effectively a "single market" for drugs and therefore, abrupt changes in policy or in consumption or trafficking patterns in one region can have significant repercussions elsewhere. Rigorous law enforcement in one country can cause displacement to areas of greater tolerance of drugs or where enforcement is less efficient.

Those who 'launder' money operate where legislation is least effective against them and dealers follow normal marketing strategies which maximise their profits in the least difficult way. Evidence of this can be seen in the activities of multinational tobacco companies which target the areas of least resistance where an uninformed clientele will fall easy prey to 'loss leader' techniques and glamorous advertising of harmful products.

The successful reduction in demand for opium poppy or coca leaf products could cause starvation for peasant farmers' families or the wholesale migration of such people to cities, in the search for employment. If drugs of this type were to be legalised either wholly or in part, it is likely that multinational companies would monopolise the production and manufacture of what were formerly illegal substances. The likely effect of this is that the "local" economies of underdeveloped countries where poppies and coca plants had become the staple, economic crop, such as Afghanistan, Peru or Colombia, might collapse or be seriously exploited.

Despite the international odium associated with the drug trade, the UN has taken the view that it has an obligation to assist with alternative development strategies that would alleviate any undue hardships that might accrue as a result of the adoption of different attitudes to drugs.

On the face of it, this is an argument, which is likely to engender little sympathy amongst those for whom drugs are an anathema. Nevertheless, there is an international agreement that it is important to consider the best ways in which pressures which drive farmers to the wholesale production of illicit crops might be relieved. Such consideration and assistance in the production of alternative crops would have a two-fold effect. Firstly of reducing the supply of the raw material for illicit drugs, thus enforcing demand reduction by non-availability, and secondly of preventing economic disaster for those people who livelihoods have come to depend upon an illicit trade for whatever reason. Controlled farming initiatives under government supervision would also benefit the countries involved by reducing the ecological damage that has become evident by some of the illicit farming activities that have involved deforestation and the alleged pollution of river systems in some South American countries.

It should be noted that crop spraying as part of the US initiative to reduce and eradicate the coca bush is alleged to have produced seriously adverse effects both for the environment and the health of the communities affected by the chemical spraying. However, it is also the case that huge amounts of chemicals used in clandestine laboratories are often dumped in rivers and watercourses with equally disastrous consequences. (INCB Report 2005).

Summary of arguments for prohibition:

- Legalisation/decriminalisation creates a particular risk among young persons

- Prohibition is successful;

- Legalisation would lead to increased use, addiction and associated medical costs;

- Legalisation sends the message of acceptability and harmlessness;

- The economic arguments of savings in the criminal justice system and tax revenues offsetting costs are flawed;

- Crime, drugs and violence go together and so dealers who are engaged in criminal activity will continue; drug testing of persons arrested for crime indicates a significantly high proportion of positive results;

- Those who are dependent upon drugs and who have turned to crime to support themselves and their habit will continue to engage in criminal activity to pay for 'legalised drugs'; the alternative is government subsidy of such people with a consequential increase in taxes;

- There is no justification for the medicinal use of cannabis or heroin;

- Insufficient information is available to justify legalisation;

- There is sufficient known to show that drugs are harmful and addictive;

- The whole purpose of drugs is to alter the mind;

- It is nonsense to claim that private use does not produce harm to the individual and to society;

- Legalisation would produce a huge administrative bureaucracy;

- Legalisation would not take the profit out of drugs;

- Other legal drugs such as tobacco and alcohol are traded in the black economy;

- Legalising drugs will not alter their adverse effects such as irrational and violent behaviour; legal drugs would have the same effects as illegal ones;

- There is no single answer to the drug problem – certainly not legalisation;

- The compassionate approach to drugs is to do everything possible to reduce addiction not to make it easier;

- There is International agreement that there must be unity against illicit drugs;

- Scientific research is continually identifying the dangers associated with illicit drug misuse;

- The health and wellbeing of the world is dependent upon illicit drug control.

The Problems with Harm Reduction

Harm reduction is a separate and distinct issue from demand reduction and it is not possible for nations to comply with their international treaty obligations to reduce drug demand by relying on harm reduction policies that accept and perpetuate drug use and its associated problems. Prevention is the only proven method for reducing substance misuse. When drug use is prevented consequential harms are eliminated but when harm reduction messages are promoted there is an inevitable acceptance and tolerance of drug use and the focus becomes misdirected to reducing harm rather than eliminating drug use. All drug use accepts and perpetuates the associated risks. There is no internationally accepted definition of what is meant by Harm Reduction.

The United States Drug Enforcement Administration (DEA) has defined harm reduction as: -

"A public health concept of lowering the health consequences resulting from certain behaviour. In the context of drug policy, it is often used to describe specific programmes, which attempt to lower addict/user transmission of infectious diseases. The term 'harm minimisation' is also used."

The Director of the International Harm Reduction Association, Pat O'Hare, has defined Harm Reduction as: -

'. . . a pragmatic public health policy, which recognises that people use drugs; recognises that it is unrealistic to try to stop people from using drugs in many cases and so people will continue to use drugs; and tries to reduce to a minimum the harms from drug use caused to the individual and to society.'

In 2005 the UK Harm Reduction Association (UKHRA) published its definition and identification of what it called the 'core principles' of harm reduction: ~

"Harm Reduction is a term that defines policies, programmes, services and actions that work to reduce the:

- Health;

- Social; and

- Economic

harms to:

- Individuals;
- Communities; and
- Society

that are associated with the use of drugs.

The principles of harm reduction (adapted from The Canadian Centre on Substance Abuse (CCSA):

Harm Reduction:

is pragmatic: and accepts that the use of drugs is a common and enduring feature of human experience. It acknowledges that, while carrying risks, drug use provides the user with benefits that must be taken into account if responses to drug use are to be effective. Harm Reduction recognises that containment and reduction of drug related harms is a more feasible option than efforts to eliminate drug use entirely.

Prioritises goals: harm reduction responses to drug use incorporate the notion of a hierarchy of goals, with the immediate focus on proactively engaging individuals, targeting groups, and communities to address their most compelling needs through the provision of accessible and user friendly services. Achieving the most immediate realistic goals is viewed as an essential first step toward risk-free (sic) use, or, if appropriate, abstinence.

Has humanist values: the drug user's decision to use drugs is accepted as fact. No moral judgment is made either to condemn or to support use of drugs. The dignity and rights of the drug user are respected, and services endeavour to be 'user friendly' in the way they operate. Harm reduction approaches also recognise that, for many, dependent drug use is a long-term feature of their lives and that responses to drug use have to accept this.

Focuses on risks and harms on the basis that by providing responses that reduce risk, harms can be reduced or avoided...

Does not focus on abstinence: although harm reduction supports those who seek to moderate or reduce their drug use, it neither excludes nor presumes a treatment goal abstinence...

Seeks to maximise the range of intervention options that are available, and engages in a process of identifying, measuring, and assessing the relative importance of drug-related harms and balancing costs and benefits in trying to reduce them.

The Scottish Centre for Post Qualification Pharmaceutical Education (SCPQPE) uses the following definition: -

"…the process of, gradually reducing psychological, social, medical and legal problems to a safer overall level in the context of continued drug misuse. It is an important intermediate and practical goal for drug misusers not yet able to achieve abstinence. It includes safer injecting and sexual practices to reduce the risk of HIV infection transmission by injecting drug misusers. Harm reduction can lead to harm minimisation and ideally to abstinence."

In reality, harm reduction (HR) is a wider concept than this and it has become used not only in circumstances where it is accepted that it is inevitable that some people will use/abuse drugs, but also as a device to encourage others to use drugs. In the former case, there is recognition that it is necessary to give advice and guidance on the safest ways of doing this. With intravenous drug users (IDU's), there is a need to ensure that the method of injection used avoids the risk of the spread of infection and the self infliction of damage by inexpert injecting. Advice about the use of clean needles and drug paraphernalia is said to be necessary to reduce the risk of the spread of infectious diseases, such as HIV/AIDS, and hepatitis C.

Unfortunately, 'Harm Reduction' is also an ideological position that assumes that some individuals cannot or will not make healthy decisions to discontinue drug abuse. Advocates of harm reduction in this context hold that some dangerous behaviour should be accepted by society and that those who follow the lifestyle of drug abuse should be enabled to continue in a less harmful manner. Those who oppose this position argue that drug-abusing lifestyles are often the result of treatable conditions that should not be accepted as normative. They also claim that sustained drug misuse will weaken the abuser's defences against infection, sustain the long-term risk of disease, and minimise the benefits of available treatments for HIV.

Harm reduction includes providing education on safe and protected sexual intercourse and, in some instances, the distribution of free condoms and needles/syringes as part of a Needle Exchange Programme (NEP – see later). No matter how regrettable such activities may be to the authorities, common sense, and pragmatism is involved, and there is seen to be as great a need to protect society from the adverse effects of current, illegal behaviour, as there is to eliminate the demand for drugs.

A major part of the harm reduction approach involves giving information on the effects of drugs and how to minimise the associated risks. Carried to extreme limits it has involved major tolerance and acceptance of drug use as in the "cannabis cafes" in Amsterdam and the "needle parks" in Switzerland which had one of the highest per capita rates of heroin and cocaine use in Europe.

About 1% of the Swiss general population is at risk between the ages of 15-30 (30,000 individuals who have regular, intensive and problematic use of heroin and cocaine). The authorities introduced low threshold, harm reduction programmes. In some cases, they involved basic survival skills, the provision of meals and toilet facilities and basic medical care; they included NEP's, methadone maintenance, and the provision of supervised injecting rooms.

The term is sometimes confused with legalisation or decriminalisation. The principles of harm reduction have a different basis from policies aimed at demand reduction and abstinence.

Proponents of harm reduction include those who are realistic enough to accept drug abusers and to offer them advice, whilst at the same time hoping for eventual abstinence. They include those who think that the root causes of drug abuse must be addressed before it is realistic to aim for a drug-free society.

The causes include social failures, which have allowed extensive poverty, poor housing conditions, inadequate education, low expectations, low self-esteem, and a general sense of hopelessness/helplessness, to develop at the lower end of society. These problems must also be addressed if there is to be any hope that prohibition will work. People need to be helped from the need to turn to mind-altering substances.

It has been pointed out that adverse circumstances exist at both ends of the commercial chain, with only the "middlemen" profiting. On the one hand, the peasant farmers compelled by circumstances to grow the most cost-efficient crop to avoid penury and starvation and on the other, some users who will do almost anything to acquire the drugs, which will give some respite from their social conditions. This includes a willingness to commit crime to enable and support their addictions.
These social circumstances are used to justify the arguments, not only for harm reduction, but also for a properly integrated system of control and supply of good quality substances to cater for the inevitable users in the safest and least damaging way.

Indeed, a House of Commons Select Committee (HC318-I 22.5.02) was persuaded to the view that the government should set up a programme of safe injecting houses for the purposes of evaluation with a longer-term expectation that the programme would be extended across the country. The Committee also recommended an evaluation programme of the prescription of diamorphine for heroin addicts. These recommendations were made in apparent ignorance of the criticism of the Swiss Heroin Trials by a committee of experts under the auspices of the World Health Organisation.

There is strong opposition to the wholesale adoption of all harm reduction policies because they are seen to be pandering to a dangerous and criminal activity. The strategy for dealing with a serious problem is criticised as the sending out the wrong message from a government which says that it opposes drug abuse and yet adopts policies which allow that conduct for some abusers.

For others harm reduction policies are supported to justify their assertion that by following them, crime will be reduced, dependent users will become healthier, and will be able to integrate themselves into society in a more productive way. There will be fewer social "drop outs".

This argument does not take account of the hidden dangers of persistent drug users in employment. In the United States, it is believed that over 73% of regular drug users are in employment, necessitating testing and substance abuse policies in the workplace (See later).

The ultimate objective of harm reduction policies should be the overall reduction to the minimum, of the harm caused by the illegal use of drugs but some use it as a way of promoting the legalisation of drugs.

The Frankfurt Resolution: ~

In 1990 representatives of nine European Cities met in Frankfurt and adopted what they called the "Frankfurt Resolution". The representatives proposed that: -

- The Criminal Law should be used only to suppress drug trafficking;

- Neither the consumption nor the possession of drugs for personal use should be prosecuted;

- Help should not be linked only to abstinence – survival assistance should be the first priority;

- There should be a separation in law between cannabis and other illegal drugs;

- The use, purchase and possession of cannabis should be decriminalised;

- Trade in cannabis products should be placed under legal control; and

- Prescription of drugs to addicts under medical supervision should be considered.

Several cities in European countries implemented these recommendations as far as they were able. An alternative association, known as "European Cities Against Drugs", was established to oppose any relaxation in anti-drug laws.

Clearly the medical health aspects of harm reduction have valid and sensible objectives and no real objection should be raised to educating people about the nature of drugs. The World Health Organisation (WHO) has estimated that about 40% of recent AIDS cases were caused by sharing injecting equipment, compared with 16% of cases in 1988.

The situation in Scotland has been cited as emphasising the need for such harm reduction pragmatism. In the mid 1980's the sero-positivity rate in Edinburgh (at that time widely described as the AIDS capital of Europe) where maintenance prescribing and NEP's had been opposed, rose by 50% (B.M.J. 292,pp.527-9.1986) whereas in Glasgow, less than fifty miles away, where such facilities were available, the level was less than 5%.

The most common way for transmission of AIDS/HIV+ is now through heterosexual intercourse, where the female partner is the most likely "victim". It has to be remembered that the sharing of needles and drug paraphernalia is more complex than the figures seem to indicate. The UN Report points out that in Italy, syringes are readily obtainable in any supermarket and yet that country has one of the highest HIV+ rates among IDU's. In some cases, needle sharing is part of a drug culture that occurs because the camaraderie between users is stronger than the fear of infection generated by information and education.

A significant problem with harm reduction is that in some cases the policy has become diluted by the "mixed message" that it transmits, particularly to young people, when those in authority appear to condone an inherently dangerous and criminal activity.

In the case of some teachers, they have taken the line of least resistance by trying not to be "judgmental" in their teaching by informing their pupils about drugs and the safest ways of using them, leaving the pupils to make "informed choices". Clearly, this is a "cop-out" if those who have the responsibility for educating young people do so by giving information and little guidance. This type of liberal and 'politically correct' attitude that can create greater harm than it is supposed to prevent and it has been exploited by those who use the message of harm reduction as a way of breaking down resistance to drug experimentation.

There has been a continuing debate about medical interventions in the harm reduction policy. For example, the prescription of opiates such as methadone as a substitute for heroin has caused misgivings amongst both doctors and police who have witnessed abuse in the selling on of prescribed doses, and the use of methadone in a cocktail of drugs that has often proved fatal (see later).

Similarly, the initial enthusiasm for NEP's has diminished now that there is a strong suspicion that they have become needle "give-aways" which are little more than a source of more shared needles for many, notwithstanding the obvious benefits if the exchanges are used properly (see later). In desperation, telephone help lines have been widely established to give information to those in need, but there are obvious dangers about the giving of medical advice other than directly to the recipient.

Generally, there is recognition that drug abuse can be a chronic, relapsing disorder and that total abstinence is not always possible for some people. In these cases, it is argued that help and guidance are essential no matter how much the dependent conduct may be deplored. The difficulty in assessing some programmes is the impossibility of knowing how bad things would have become without them.

Harm Reduction in extremis – the Swiss example.

Democracy is capable of allowing the subversion of the wishes of the electorate. In the case of Switzerland – perceived by many as a stable and law abiding country – an example of this emerged. Widespread increases in crime, increased and publicly visible drug abuse, significant urban deterioration, and a dropping off in previously high standards of education became apparent.

In the mid-1980's, the Zurich town council was taken over by a socialist-environmentalist coalition. There were links between one of the councillors and the Italian Radical Party whose support derived largely from areas with a high density of Mafia supporters. There followed a liberalisation approach towards drugs in Zurich, which included NEP's and the opening of Platzpitz (Needle Park) where harm reduction policies were followed. Several thousand addicts received methadone treatment and many of the 20,000 dependants were HIV+.

Despite this liberal approach, organised criminals continued to control the price of drugs and crime increased. The death rate amongst drug-users was nearly 2 times higher than that of non-users. The Needle Park was closed in 1992 but a second one was opened in the summer of that year at Letten Station where the activities of the addicts were again open to public view. Children on their way to school were able to witness the drug taking activities.

There was a general anti-drug stance with the majority of the population but the 'legalisers' continued to advance harm reduction as the best way of dealing with the drug problem. By May of 1995, the number of drug addicts in the country had doubled and that doubling occurred again to November 1996.

Those opposed to NEP's and the tolerance at Letten Station called for a referendum against legalisation. The anti-legalisation referendum was opposed, by some members of the press, some wealthy business people and by some government officials. A prominent banker with the Swiss Bank Corporation persuaded many business people to sign an anti-referendum document and supported the legal distribution of heroin. These business leaders agreed to the employment of addicts, who were being supported on legally prescribed heroin in the hope of assisting their re-integration into society.

This support for the prescription of heroin to help addicts was seen as endorsing the legalisation movement and gave it credibility to such an extent that 71% of those who voted supported legalisation. Only 30% of eligible voters actually voted but this 'democratic process' had been manipulated in an attempt to legalise the distribution of heroin to addicts.

In November 1998, another referendum was held to allow a constitutional amendment, which would have legalised "the consumption, cultivation, or possession of drugs and their acquisition for personal use". The proposed amendment would have allowed narcotic drugs consumed for non-medical reasons to be available without prescription. 74% voted against that proposal.

(References –"Radicals Hijack Swiss Idyll" Patricia Morgan,
Sunday Telegraph 2.5.1995, "Drug Politics" David C. Jordan 1999,).

Needle Exchange Programmes.

Needle Exchange Programmes were established in the U.K. in the 1980s. The original intention of these programmes was based on the hypothesis that they would play an important part in preventing the transmission of HIV and limit the spread of AIDs. In the 1990s, this aim was enlarged to include prevention of the spread of other blood-borne viruses such as hepatitis B, C, and D. In 2002 the Government stated that 27 million needles p.a. were 'exchanged' in England.

In Scotland, the exchanges are operated either by drug agencies or by some pharmacies (9%). Approximately 17% of the pharmacies offer injecting equipment for sale in accordance with Government guidelines. The minimum service provided by a pharmacy should be the provision of:

- a supply of clean injecting equipment and equipment for safe disposal, without charge;

- a safe disposal system for used, returned equipment;

- new needles and syringes in exchange for used equipment;

- written information about HIV, Hepatitis and other blood-borne diseases and safer sexual practices;

- written advice about agencies able to give confidential advice on drug use;

- advice, about safer injecting techniques.

Although these programmes are called Needle Exchanges the reality is that most of them operate without insisting on the return of used equipment. It is claimed that this is a pragmatic approach that recognises that certain people will inject drugs regardless of whether needles are given out and that it is better that they should have access to clean needles rather than take the risk of sharing a dirty needle.

These programmes continue to be subjected to much criticism largely because the research that has been carried out in the USA and Australia raises serious questions about their efficacy and the validity of the original hypothesis upon which they were based. A report published in October 2005 by the Health Protection Agency indicated that during 2004 new infections of HIV and Hepatitis C increased amongst intravenous drug users and there was evidence of continuing Hepatitis B virus infections as well as Hepatitis A. An update to the report also showed that up to 50% of injecting drug users were unaware that they had become infected and a significant number admitted to sharing needles and other paraphernalia.

("Shooting Up: infections among injecting drug users
in the United Kingdom 2004 an update October 2005)

In November 2005 The Prison Reform Trust and the National AIDS Trust called for condoms, disinfecting tablets, clean needles and healthcare information to be made available within prisons which they said were failing effectively to provide healthcare for prisoners with Hepatitis C and HIV. A joint study revealed that despite high levels of HIV and hepatitis among prisoners, prisons in Britain are continuing to provide "inconsistent and often sub-standard healthcare". Over half the prisons were found to have no sexual health policy and 9% of male prisoners and 11% of female prisoners were known to have Hepatitis C (20 times the UK rate). The idea of distributing clean needles was said to be a pragmatic approach to dealing with a serious health risk.

Those opposed to the NEPs claim that the science is uncertain and that there is little scientific or empirical evidence to demonstrate that they reduce the spread of infection. Indeed, there is evidence to show that, a massive increase in the spread of Hepatitis C coincided with the introduction of NEPs.

About 4 million Americans and at least 50,000 British citizens are infected by HCV, and it is thought that 60% of this number represented intravenous drug users (IDUs) at the time of infection. In the UK, it is predicted that HCV will be the biggest single cause of a demand for liver transplants within the next decade. It has been estimated that over 150 million people have Hepatitis C world-wide. Research, published in the journal "Annals of Internal Medicine" (16.1.01) indicated that excessive use of alcohol by those affected by Hepatitis C increases the likelihood of cirrhosis of the liver, which in turn enhances the risk of cancer. Information released by the UK Government Health Protection Agency in December 2003 indicated that two in five injectors share their needles with others regardless of the health risks. Almost three fifths of those infected are unaware of their condition. Transmission of Hep A.B and C are increasing although the transmission of HIV in the UK by needles is said to be rare.

(Shooting-Up-Infections among Injecting Drug Users
in the UK in 2002 updated December 2003).

In the USA, the former Drug Czar, General McCaffrey, blocked Federal funding of NEPs. His reasoning was based on a report on the Vancouver NEP which distributed more than 4.5 million needles a year without even the pretence of asking for used needles in exchange for new. This figure is predicted rapidly to grow to 10 million at present (2002) user rates. In addition to the lack of definitive research evidence to demonstrate that NEPs achieve what they were supposed to, the concerns were: -

Public Health risks may outweigh potential benefits. There is strong evidence in North America and in the UK to suggest that heroin and cocaine use is increasing among IDUs and it is argued that the risk that NEPs might encourage that use outweighs any possible public health benefits. Research has demonstrated that the rate of infection in the general population is declining regardless of NEPs and that this success has been wrongly attributed to the provision of clean needles. Vancouver has the highest death rate from overdoses (particularly of heroin) the rise coinciding with the introduction of the NEP. In 1988 there were just 18 deaths; by 1993 the number had risen to 200 p.a. and, in 1998 the deaths were running at 10 per week. Needles are now used to inject cocaine (previously the traditional method of ingestion was by "snorting") where an addict may attempt up to 50 "hits" a day. Coincidentally heroin abuse has increased significantly since the proliferation of NEPs across America. It should be noted that this phenomenon occurred elsewhere, particularly in Scotland, and may be more to do with an increase in the supply of cheaper, higher purity heroin rather than NEPs.

Treatment must be regarded as a priority. Where budgets are restricted, it is thought that it is better to treat addicts than to support a strategy that may encourage addiction.

Federal support of NEPs may undermine support for drug-control programmes. Spending Federal money on NEPs detracts from spending on AIDS research, treatment, and prevention programmes.

Supporting NEPs sends the wrong message to children. Lending official support to a programme that appears to encourage addiction and illegal conduct, is inconsistent with the goals of a national youth-orientated, anti-drug campaign and sending a "mixed message" would threaten to undermine the credibility of other anti-drug initiatives.

NEPs do nothing to ameliorate the impact of drug use on disadvantaged neighbourhoods. NEPs are usually located in impoverished neighbourhoods. The programmes attract addicts and result in a concentration of the negative consequences of drug use including criminal activity.

The major concerns with NEPs in North America seem to turn around the lack of any evidence at all that they are beneficial and every indication, from the Vancouver experience, that they create thousands of extra "shared" needles (Vancouver Drug Use Epidemiology Report 2003).

The development of these programmes was based on a theory which has not been validated and against which there is ample suspicion that the programmes actually encourage drug abuse, assist the spread of infections and defeat other anti-drug initiatives.

Nevertheless, support for such programmes remains in some quarters and the State of New York approved legislation, which commenced on 1st January 2001, permitting pharmacists to sell up to 10 syringes at a time, at their discretion, to individual customers. There are over 1800 pharmacists in the State authorised to sell needles under this legislation and opponents fear that this will merely add to the supply of shared needles amongst dependent users. Reporters have claimed that they were able to purchase syringes with needles for as little as 50 cents each, in lower East Side, Brooklyn Heights and Jamaica, Queens. (Daily News- 9.1.01)

In Scotland there is no officially published information available that assesses the efficacy or otherwise of Needle Exchanges. Separate budgetary allocations are made for Health Authorities who undertake NEPs and a review by the Scottish Office of HIV health promotion strategy was published in 2002 but this did not add much weight in support of NEPs.

In 1997, The National Institutes of Health Consensus Panel Report on HIV Prevention praised the NEP in Glasgow, but did not refer to the massive heroin epidemic, which appears to reflect the experience of North America. Evidence from Australia, has raised serious doubts about the hypothesis that ready access to clean injecting equipment would play an important role in the control of HIV transmission. It points to a contemporaneous rise in the spread of hepatitis C among IDUs, which was also apparent in Glasgow and other cities throughout the UK.

Much of the support for NEPs in both North America and the UK appears to be based on anecdotal evidence and the use of statistics, which some claim have been demonstrated to be unreliable. What is of great concern is that after so many years there has been no official assessment of this 'act of faith' when there has been a concomitant rise in drug use.

A trawl of the scientific literature has failed to produce any conclusive evidence that NEPs reduce the spread of AIDS/HIV and Hepatitis C or that they do not encourage drug use. Indeed, the reverse of that hypothesis might well be true, given the evidence that there is a massive increase in heroin use and that drug related deaths amongst intravenous drug users "sky-rocketed" across Scotland, particularly in Aberdeen and Glasgow.

There are fears in North America that the support for NEP s is part of an International drug legalisation, campaign which will lead to the free supply of heroin as has occurred in Switzerland and The Netherlands. There are also legitimate concerns that NEPs are acting directly in contradiction to the philosophy behind the Drugs Courts, which depend upon a "carrot and stick" approach in order to persuade users to refrain from drug use altogether.

A survey, in mid-1997, by the Family Research Council in the U.S.A., conducted on its behalf by a Washington, D.C. polling company, indicated substantial opposition to NEPs. Opposition rested on the belief that NEPs are not the most effective use of public funds to prevent AIDS/HIV. NEPs are thought to exacerbate other social problems. According to this poll, substantial majorities believed that AIDS prevention should focus on drug treatment instead of what are, in effect, "needle give-aways" with strong evidence that thousands of these clean needles will become "dirty" when shared with other addicts.

Simultaneously maintaining and trying to reduce the harm in an inherently destructive practice and lifestyle is thought to be both unsuccessful and hypocritical. By a margin of 56% to 34%, Americans concluded that Government-funded NEPs represented an official endorsement of illegal drug use.

Handbooks on safer methods of injecting drugs issued by drug agencies in the UK acknowledge that there is no completely safe way of injecting drugs and that the practice carries with it a much higher risk of overdose, vein damage and infection than smoking, swallowing or "snorting". The main risks associated with injecting are:

- HIV infection;

- Hepatitis infection;

- Vein damage;

- Overdose;

- Infection from bacteria

- An increase in the level of dependency

There is also the danger that an IDU will develop a needle psychosis or "fixation" in which there is a psychological addiction to and dependence upon the use of the needle particularly when IDUs share and inject together. The rituals associated with injecting and "sharing" can be as psychologically powerful and attractive as the substance dependence.

Clearly, opinions are divided on the efficacy of NEPs and there is evidence on both sides of the argument. However, the overwhelming evidence is that NEPs are usually "give-aways" in the hope that users will act responsibly. While a controlled programme may offer some benefits for public health and may reduce the spread of blood borne diseases in some cases, there is evidence to show that the reverse effect is also evident. One has only to walk down Hastings Street in Vancouver to see the huge numbers of addicts who are openly injecting in public places. Many are sharing needles, which are distributed from street stalls, which also promote the use of cannabis and other drugs. The harm that can occur from uncontrolled distribution is very apparent and something more needs to be done to help dependent people instead of adopting a "one size fits all" approach to a serious problem.

An article in the European Journal of Public Health, 2003;13:252-258 (Amundsen EJ, Eskild A, Stigum H, Smith E, AAlen OO.) has reported that a comparison between the prevention strategies of Norway, Sweden, and Denmark demonstrated that HIV counselling and testing may be more effective that needle handouts. Sweden and Norway had significantly lower rates of HIV in IV users as compared with Denmark

In April 2004 the results of a study conducted at the McLean Hospital Alcohol and Drug abuse Research Center in Belmont, Massachusetts and Harvard Medical School indicate that drug abuse may increase HIV infection risk by compromising the immune system. The researchers say that cocaine itself has a direct biological effect that may decrease an abusers ability to resist infection. The new data may explain why drug abusers have higher rates of infections than other 'risk' groups and why areas with longstanding and high volume needle exchanges have failed to curtail the spread of HIV and hepatitis among the injection using population. The only scientifically proven prevention strategies are said to be prevention and treatment. (NIDA - Halpern, J.H., et al. Diminished interleukin-6 response to proinflammatory challenge in men and women after intravenous cocaine administration. Journal of Clinical Endocrinology and metabolism 88 (3): 1188-1193, 2003.). It remains the case that there are few scientific reviews of the harm reduction programmes driven by the ideological position adopted by some advocates.

The substitute prescribing of Methadone.

Methadone is prescribed as a substitute for opiates (heroin) it is a Class A drug and it is legal to possess it only by prescription. It often occurred that prescriptions were made out to cover dosage for a week or even a month, but because the methadone was finding its way onto the illicit market, supervised consumption can be arranged at the request of the prescribing doctor. In Scotland, one third of the methadone clients receive a supervised daily dose.

The main aim of prescribing methadone is to reduce harm by: -

- maintaining contact with the patient;
- deterring the use of street drugs of doubtful purity;
- encouraging a shift from a more dangerous form of drug misuse;
- controlled dosage of the drug, with the aim of weaning the patient away from it altogether.

Controlled consumption of methadone is not compulsory and some doctors have given prescriptions for a week or ten days' supply. Methadone has a street value and within hours of receiving a fraudulently obtained prescription, for ten days' supply a user in the North East of Scotland was able to sell it for £270. That amount of money was used to purchase an eighth of an ounce of heroin, which could be sold on as 30 'wraps' netting £600 for the seller. The whole cycle could then occur again.

(Aberdeen and District Independent 7.10.99).

The chances of methadone prescribing being helpful in reducing drug related harm and in assisting the user to eventual abstention are enhanced where additional help is offered such as advice and support, counselling and supervised, structured programmes leading to demand reduction and abstention.

Substitute prescribing has been criticised on the grounds that, it has a high dependency potential and is more addictive than heroin. It has been claimed that methadone causes no physical damage to the brain, liver, kidneys or bones. However, regular users have stated that it does affect their bones and rots their teeth, although the latter may be more to do with dental hygiene. Advisory leaflets about the use of methadone draw attention to the need to take particular care of the teeth, because it is usually prescribed in a liquid syrup form.

A survey undertaken in the cities of Liverpool and Manchester by "The Big Issue in the North" charity in 1999 revealed the following information about methadone: -

- Of those on prescribed methadone 80% also used street drugs on a weekly basis, particularly heroin. 44% on prescribed methadone used heroin on a daily basis.

- Although a quarter of users said they received counselling, many did not and twice as many said it was important as actually received it. Many users felt that doctors who knew little about the overall drug problem had prescribed them methadone.

- 17% of all those receiving prescribed methadone were injecting heroin at least occasionally and were not using needle exchanges.

- Virtually no respondents said that the drug services were aiming at providing a co-ordinated package of treatment including non-medical services to help them make progress in other areas of life. Most were unemployed.

- Many users had been attending services for a long time, most between 3-8 years and many felt that they were being maintained on an addictive drug as bad as heroin. Some users had been on methadone treatment for as long as 12 years.

Research in the USA resulted in scientists announcing (May 2000 "USA Today" 31.5.00) that they were ready to launch alternative anti-addiction drugs for heroin addicts. The new drugs are considered less addictive than methadone. One such drug is called Soboxone and is a combination of buprenorphine and naloxone in a once-a-day pill; the drug was expected to be approved by the US Food and Drug Administration in

September 2000 but final approval was not forthcoming until October 2002. The significant difference about drugs containing buprenorphine and methadone is that it is thought to be virtually impossible to overdose on heroin when buprenorphine is used.

Subutex, which contains the synthetic opiate buprenorphine, is manufactured. in the UK and is available in pill form by prescription in 30 countries as a supervised treatment for heroin withdrawal. Illegal in the Caucasus state of Georgia, the pills are smuggled into the country and where drug addicts dissolve the pills and inject them. The INCB says there is an 80% increase in this drug abuse since 2003.

Federal officials began a national campaign to educate doctors and patients about buprenorphine and the authorisation allows them to treat addiction to heroin or other opioids, including prescription pain killers just like any other medical condition. The Director of Treatment and Research at NIDA, Dr Frank Vocci said that many addicts might have to stay on the drug for life - the goal is to get patients to come off heroin.

Buprenorphine was originally tested as a pain medication and was studied for more than 15 years as a potential treatment for addiction at NIDA and Johns Hopkins Bayview Medical Center. The tablet works by satisfying an addict's craving for opioids (heroin, morphine, codeine etc) without producing a "high". In some cases, it has the added benefit of making a patient sick with withdrawal like symptoms if narcotics are used. It is not necessarily more effective than methadone, but it may be more palatable to addicts, and it may take the pressure off methadone clinics. Buprenorphine is widely abused by addicts. Reckitt Benckiser, manufacturer of Subutex has designed another buprenorphine-based drug to treat opiate dependency. Called Suboxone, this drug is said to be "less abuseable," and has been licensed for use in the US

In November 2003 the Health Department in San Francisco began dispensing naloxone, a controversial anti-overdose medication, to heroin addicts at a city sponsored Needle Exchange Programme. Some doctors criticise this move as they say that it could encourage further addiction. This programme requires people who receive the drug to be trained in how to administer the drug and how to perform rescue techniques to assist overdose victims. Medical experts say that addicts are unreliable and are the wrong people to be involved in administering medication. Naxolone is mainly used against heroin but it is said to be effective with other opiates such as morphine and oxycontin.

Methadone and Pregnancy.

Results from a study carried out in a major methadone maintenance programme in a Switzerland perinatal centre are reported to have shown a high rate of maternal complications in women enrolled in the programme between 1996-2001. Prospective data based on 89 pregnant opiate addicts and their neonates apparently showed 73% of the women with maternal complications and 34% of the neonates with foetal complications. 64% of the women were users of cocaine and/or heroin. Among the polydrug users, birth weight was lower in the near exclusive methadone users. The investigators concluded that methadone maintenance is "ineffective in preventing pregnancy exposure to additional illicit drug consumption". The only alternative treatment of opiate addiction in pregnancy, according to the authors, is active detoxification, which carries a high risk of failure with approximately 50% of the women in the study returning to methadone during pregnancy.

(Kashiwagi M, Arilettaz R, Lauper U, et al: Acta Obstet Gynecol Scand 2005: 84[2]: 140-144.
See also: American Journal of Obstetrics and Gynaecology, September 2005.)

CHAPTER 5
Cannabis

Cannabis is the most widely produced, trafficked, and consumed illicit drug but there are no reliable production estimates available. Rising levels of seizures and evidence of increasing consumption, suggest that output is increasing (UNODC – Global Illicit Drug Trends 2003 and UN World Drug Report 2006). Abuse increases have been reported in almost all regions, including Africa where cannabis remains the most widely abused drug. About two thirds of the 86 countries reporting to UNODC in 2002 indicated higher levels of abuse in line with greater seizures (up 40% from 1998).The Executive Director of UNODC, Antonio Maria Costa expressed great concern about the cannabis pandemic and pointed out that traffickers have invested heavily in increasing the potency – and therefore – the attractiveness – of cannabis. He called on all Governments to do more to reduce drug demand in general but particularly cannabis. He stated that the characteristics of cannabis are now little different from those of other plant based drugs such as cocaine and heroin.

(World Drug Report 2006.)

Until recently, seizures of cannabis plants, which are regarded as an indicator of the efforts made by Governments to eradicate cannabis plantations, appear to have been declining. This may indicate that some Governments have given a lesser priority to the eradication of the crop and that the tolerant attitude towards so called 'soft' drugs by some European Governments may be undermining the resolve in some producing countries. Some developing countries, especially in Africa, have repeatedly expressed concern about how the policies in some developed countries have compromised their drug control efforts.

Positive trends reported in the USA show that abuse of cannabis (annual prevalence) has fallen 10% since 1997 and 30% since the late 1970s.

Cannabis - some history of the drug: -

Cannabis sativa is the Latin name for a hemp plant that grows wild in both temperate and tropical climates. It is also cultivated illegally, especially indoors, and hydroponically.

The plant is thought to have originated in Central Asia. Certainly, it was recorded in China some 5000 years ago where it was cultivated for fibre and oil. It was not used psychoactively until the 1800s when it became a substance to be avoided by rational people because it was known to disturb the equilibrium of the brain and make some users "see devils".

From China, it is thought to have migrated to the Indian sub-continent where it was used ritually in temples. It is mentioned in the "Atharva Veda" (2000BC) as a sacred plant. Ancient Hindus used it for its medicinal properties. From India, it spread to Persia and Assyria in the 8th century where it was known as 'quanabu' or 'kanabas'. Herodutus reports that the barbarian Scythians intoxicated themselves with the vapours from burning hemp.

Apparently it was unknown to the early Egyptians but the Greeks and Romans used it for rope and sail making. The physician Galen described some medicinal uses of hemp and there was widespread use in the Middle East after the rise of Islam. The prophet Muhammad forbade the use of wine but he did not exclude cannabis and it was not until the eighteenth century that the Muslim faith banned the use of hashish for the faithful because it affected ritual prayers by clouding the mind. {In the 21st century, the Taliban in Afghanistan justified the trade in opium and heroin because its use was for kafirs (unbelievers)}.

Its use in the USA was mainly for the manufacture of rope, twine, and sailcloth. In 1850 it was introduced to medicine for the treatment of epilepsy, rheumatism, menstrual cramps, cholera, convulsions, chorea, hysteria, depression, insanity, tetanus, gout, neuralgia and uterine haemorrhage. It was withdrawn from the pharmacopoeia in 1942. Its first recorded use for pleasure was by black musicians who were referred to as "deviants". It was brought under Federal control by the passing of the Marihuana Tax Act, 1937; however smoking this substance did not permeate mainstream society until after the Second World War.

Cannabis was first used in British medical practise in 1830 by O'Shaugnessy, who had observed its use in India as an analgesic; it was dropped from the pharmacopoeia when more reliable medicines were developed. It was used in France by Moreau who wrote "Hashish intoxication and Mental illness" in 1840.

Current position:

Cannabis is the most widely abused drug listed in international control treaties and it affects practically every country. There has been a rapid proliferation of cultivation, mainly indoors which has yielded cannabis with increasingly high tetrahydrocannabinol (THC) content. These "Grow Ops" became popular in the 1990s in North America to the extent that Canadian Police have stated that they are sometimes overwhelmed by the problem. In the twenty- first century home grown cannabis became a significant industry in the UK with gangs operating sophisticated cannabis farms on a massive scale.

Modern cannabis is a very different commodity from that which was used by the "Flower-Power" generation of the 1960s although this is not always realised by parents who 'experimented' with the drug in that era.

Cannabis - the drug:

The plant contains 400 known chemicals but it is noted for approximately 66 cannabinoids. Most of the cannabinoids are closely related and so it does not follow that there are 66 different effects or interactions.

Cannabinoids fall into 10 groups and many of them differ only slightly. Delta 9 tetrahydrocannabinol (THC) is the chemical thought to be responsible for the psychoactive effect associated with cannabis but others such as cannabidiol and cannabinol may modify the effects of THC.

Cannabinoids are described as being lipophilic because they are retained in the fatty tissues of the body and released gradually into the blood stream over a period of days; they are highly soluble in fatty fluids but not in water. Indeed, THC is so lipophilic that it is often described as being "greasy" and it takes days for it to be metabolized by the liver and eliminated from the body. Tests have indicated traces of cannabis in the body up to 4 months after last declared ingestion although it is more common for traces to remain for 4-5 weeks. Unlike alcohol which is water soluble, and is broken down by a healthy liver at the rate of 1 unit per hour cannabis effects remain for a much longer period. In the case of a regular user of cannabis, smoking (or ingesting by other means) once or twice a week will result in the body never being free from traces of THC.

The term cannabinoid includes any substance which activates cannabis receptors in the brain including synthetic (eg nabilone) and endogenous (eg anandamide) compounds.

There are three drugs derived from the cannabis plant: -

Marijuana - is the most common illegal drug of abuse; the term refers to the leaves and flowers of cannabis plants. They are used to produce a substance similar in appearance to tobacco, but with widely differing degrees of strength depending upon where and how it was grown. The amounts of cannabinoids in a plant vary with growing conditions, including humidity, temperature, and soil nutrients. The chemical stability of cannabinoids in harvested material is affected by the conditions under which it is stored.

"Skunk" and Nederweed (Dutch Nederweit) are particularly potent varieties of cannabis with a high THC level ranging between 9-35%. Nederweit has been specially cultivated in Holland since 1977 when the Dutch Parliament permitted the toleration of cannabis and the licensing of the now infamous "cannabis cafes" or coffee shops.

The current potency of "Nederweit" is on average ten times that of the cannabis commonly available at the time of the liberalisation of attitudes. The Government of The Netherlands introduced legislation to ban the production of all indoor grown cannabis because of the increasingly serious dimension of the problem (INCB Annual Report 1999) but this law appears to be "more honoured in the breach than the observance". It also commissioned research (2001) into the harmful effects of the high THC content of Dutch grown Nederweit. This stronger variety of cannabis was reported to be available in the UK in 1994.

The International Narcotics Control Board called on all countries where indoor cultivation has proliferated to take urgent counter-measures and to consider the introduction of legislation to deal with the problem (INCB Report 1999). In 2004 the indoor growing of cannabis in Canada was reported to be at a very high level with police losing the ability to keep track of the increasing number of "grow-ops"". Canada now has the dubious distinction of being a main source country for marijuana exportation and there has been a significant increase in the amounts of marijuana being seized at the border with the USA.

In May 2004 the Ministry of Health in Holland started to issue stronger health warnings on the use of soft drugs and the Dutch Government announced its intention of prohibiting 'drug tourism'. A government representative announced the possibility that cannabis with a particularly high THC content may be classified as a hard drug. In May 2005 it was reported by Reuters that the Dutch Government was examining ways in which non-registered visitors to The Netherlands could be prohibited from using the coffee shops as a way of cutting down on drug tourism.

The home grown varieties of cannabis, which are common in Holland are exported widely throughout Europe and North America (in the form of seeds for cultivation) and command a higher price than normal cannabis because of the higher potency. The seeds and growing paraphernalia are marketed on the Internet and according to the INCB Report the targets frequently are school children.

This surge in home grown cannabis has been facilitated by the unrestricted sale of cannabis seeds and growing accessories in some "hemp shops". The US Government has acted to restrict hemp products but to date the UK Government has not prevented the sale of either seeds or growing equipment.

Hashish - is a resinous substance with a high THC content; it is produced from the cannabis plant after it has been dried and is compressed into cakes, sheets, or balls from which pieces are broken and smoked in pipes. Occasionally hashish is baked in cakes or included in chocolate bars and eaten. In one instance in Canada, analysts for the RCMP measured the THC content of some seized cannabis resin at an astonishing 78%. Three quarters of seizures of resin in 2002 were in Western Europe.

Cannabis Oil - hash or Hemp oil is produced by extracting cannabinoids from the plant using a solvent. It is a concentrate in the form of a brown viscous liquid with an average THC potency of 15% but in some cases, levels have reached between 30-60%. Small amounts are dropped onto normal cigarettes and this produces a similar effect to smoking a joint.

Synthetic THC has been produced for medicinal use in the form of Marinol, in the USA and Nabilone marketed as Cesamet, in the UK. These have been used under medical supervision and prescription for the control of nausea and vomiting after chemotherapy treatment, and as a stimulant for eating in severe cancer-related anorexia and AIDS cases.

These products have been criticised for being slow-acting which in the case of nausea and vomiting, is a distinct disadvantage. (The packages containing these medicines draw attention to the fact that THC encourages both physical and psychological dependence, causes mood changes and has been responsible for memory loss and psychosis, impairment of co-ordination and perception, and can cause complications in pregnancy).

The effects of cannabis use:

Cannabis products are normally smoked in the form of cigarettes referred to as 'joints' or 'spliffs' and sometimes (in the USA) in hollowed out cigars filled with cannabis referred to as 'blunts' (after the name of the cigar - "Phillies Blunt Cigar"). It can be inhaled through pipes and consumed in food, although this method of consumption is not as common as smoking. Smoking materials are sometimes laced with a variety of adulterants including Class A drugs in the UK, phencyclidine (PCP or 'angel dust') in the USA and formaldehyde, which alters the toxicity and 'mind-altering' effects significantly. It was reported in 2001(ONDCP Pulse Check) that dealers in the USA were lacing marijuana with these substances and with powder cocaine in order to enhance the demand for the harder drugs. In the Southern States laced joints are sometimes referred to as 'Sherman Sticks'.

In North America, cannabis products extracted from a plant known as sinsemilla (Spanish = without seed) is used regularly because of its high THC content. In 1974, the Drug Enforcement Administration reported that the average THC content of marijuana was between 0.5 -1% but by 1994 it had increased to 5%. In the case of sinsemilla it can be as high as 17%, which is very powerful but still only half the potency of the strongest varieties of Nederweit (35%).

Experienced users say that the initial effect of the drug depends, to a certain extent, on the circumstances in which it is taken and the expectations of the users. Often first time users report their disappointment at failing to experience any form of stimulation. Effects are usually felt within the first few minutes after inhalation and a peak is reached between 10-30 minutes after use. Small doses tend to create a dreamlike state of relaxation but often there is a heightened awareness of senses such as vision, smell, taste, and hearing with some reports of users speaking about "smelling sounds" and "hearing colours", a condition known as synaesthesia (the interchange of senses).

Casual observers may not notice a state of intoxication in cannabis users but its effects can inhibit normal self-control and accidents are more likely after use. Strong doses and regular use can produce significant distortions in co-ordination abilities and awareness of things such as the passage of time. Many studies have demonstrated that cannabis and THC administered acutely can produce dose-related impairments to psychomotor and cognitive skills. There are noticeable effects on short-term memory, vigilance, and hand-eye co-ordination. Perception of time and distance impairs the performance of complex tasks requiring divided attention, such as flying an aeroplane, driving a motor vehicle, or working complex machinery. In May 2005 the University of Auckland, New Zealand conducted research which showed that heavy cannabis users are 10 times more likely to be injured, or to injure others, in car accidents

Experiences differ, but many have reported impaired thought and memory processes and the inability to perform simple tasks and calculations. The user is seldom aware of being adversely affected at the time. Adverse effects are even more apparent when cannabis use is combined with alcohol. However, it is not thought to increase risk taking behaviour as is the case with alcohol, and it is not normally associated with violence although there are reports of aggressive behaviour where a dependent or regular user has discontinued use of the drug or is denied access to normal supplies. (There are reports of marijuana use being associated with violence in the USA - see Marijuana Use amongst Adolescents: The New Epidemic - Drew W Edwards, MS April 2002).).

Acute cannabis intoxication can lead to panic attacks, paranoia, and confused feelings and in the case of people with a predisposition to mental illness, especially schizophrenia, it can exacerbate that condition. Cannabis psychosis is common and although the panic attacks are usually short-lived in some cases acute intoxication produces a psychotic state that may continue for some time and require treatment with anti-psychotic drugs. In a few instances, such an episode may be the start of a long-lasting psychotic illness. In January 2004 Professor Robin Murray, head of psychiatry at the Institute of Psychiatry issued a warning to the Government that inner-city London psychiatric services were nearing a crisis point with up to 80% of all new psychotic cases reporting a history of cannabis use.

Professor Murray stated that people who used cannabis in their teenage years were up to seven times more likely to develop psychosis, delusional episodes, or manic depression.

Professor Murray's findings appear to have been endorsed by research published in November 2005 from Aarhus Psychiatric Hospital in Denmark which showed that cannabis smokers who develop what may appear to be temporary psychotic symptoms have a high risk of progressing to severe psychiatric disorders including paranoid schizophrenia (British Journal of Psychiatry November 2005 – Mikkel Arendt et al).

After the report of the Advisory Council on the Misuse of Drugs in 2002 there were four studies indicating that cannabis use, particularly in young people, can increase significantly the likelihood of the onset of psychosis. The use of cannabis drastically reduces recovery for those who may be mentally ill. Hallucinations and fantasies may be experienced with high doses and "flashbacks" have been known to occur.

The health risks associated with Cannabis use.

Most cannabis is smoked and this produces significant health risks. Cannabis smokers suffer from the same hazards as tobacco smokers – lung cancer, bronchitis, emphysema, and asthma, but the combination of cannabis with tobacco exacerbates these conditions significantly. Respiratory and pulmonary toxicity are major complications caused by smoking cannabis. Research published by the University of Birmingham (UK) in 2003 reinforced the dangerous potential of regularly smoking cannabis, particularly for young people. Smoking cannabis on a regular basis - 3-4 joints per week over a period of 5 years can impair lung function and deny the body antioxidants that protect cells against damage that can lead to heart disease and cancer. The British Thoracic society registered its concern and called for further research.

Tar levels associated with cannabis smoking have been reported at 70% higher than in tobacco smoke and cannabis smoke is reported to contain up to 3000 chemicals, including cyanide, which are delivered directly to the lungs. Young people who smoke cannabis with tobacco have been found to have pre-cancerous lesions in their lungs normally detected only in middle-aged people who have been long-term tobacco smokers.

There is a difference between types of inhalation used for ordinary cigarettes and joints of cannabis. Research has shown that cannabis is often smoked with an inhalation one third greater and a retention time four times longer than tobacco. In these circumstances more inhaled particles are deposited in the respiratory tract and lungs, with a greater potential for damage. (Dr Steven M Dubinett, head of Research Team at UCLA Jonsson Cancer Center- Journal of Immunology July 2000). The World Health Organisation has found cannabis smoking to be three times more carcinogenic than smoking cigarettes.

Research published in January 2000 by the Memorial Sloan-Kettering Cancer Center in New York claimed that marijuana smoke is higher in tar and carcinogens than tobacco smoke. It said that regular smokers of cannabis can be 30 times more likely to develop cancer of the neck, throat, mouth and larynx than those who had never smoked that substance. The research indicated that amongst those who used cannabis once a day, the risk of developing tumours was 2•1 times greater than among those who had never used it. Among those who smoked it more than once a day the risk increased to 4•9 times greater. The risk to those who smoked cigarettes as well as cannabis was said to be 36 times greater than among those who did not smoke at all. Smoking cannabis is thought to have a similar effect on lung cancer as smoking tobacco.

Research indicates that for older smokers of cannabis there is a 4•8 times greater risk of their having a heart attack, in the first hour after smoking the drug than there is amongst those who do not smoke at all.

("Circulation" June 2001 - Journal of the American Heart Assn. - Dr Murray Mittelman, Director of Cardiovascular Epidemiology, Beth Israel Deaconess Medical Centre, Boston.).

A report by the Advisory Council on the Misuse of Drugs (March 2002) said that smoking cannabis presents a real risk to health, potentially similar to that of tobacco and perhaps presenting a greater risk since cannabis has a higher concentration of certain, carcinogens. However, it went on to suggest that there are factors, which may mitigate that risk.

In general, cannabis users are thought to smoke fewer cigarettes per day than tobacco smokers and most are thought to give up the habit by their 30s. The report suggested that these factors would reduce the long-term exposure that is known to be the critical factor in cigarette induced lung cancer. This is at odds with an assessment made by the American National Institute of Health in 1999 which indicated that smoking just five joints of cannabis per week can equate with smoking a packet of cigarettes a day for a week.

Research indicates that cannabis smoking disrupts the hormonal balance and this gives rise to the suspicion that it can affect fertility and there have been reports of disturbance in growth and of delayed sexual maturity. (Ramstrom page 70)

Cannabis is known to affect adversely, the central nervous, cardiovascular, respiratory, reproductive, and neuro-psychological systems; it is thought to affect the immune system as well although more research is necessary to confirm this. The negative effects of cannabis have been found to include impotence in men, a reduction in the sperm count and alterations to the reproductive hormonal system. In women interference in the menstrual cycle has occurred.

The possible adverse effects on the immune system of some users means that they may be more susceptible to diseases and infections and thus would develop more severe symptoms and experience longer recovery times.

In Holland there is increasing concern that the use of Nederweit is creating large numbers of de-motivated young people, who are both drug dependent and "chronically passive". This condition is sometime described as the 'amotivational syndrome'.

There is evidence that individuals who start to smoke marijuana at an early age-while the brain is still developing-show deficits in cognition that are not seen in individuals who begin use of the drug when they are older; the reasons for this difference are unclear. Scientists from the Harvard Medical School and from the intramural research program of the National Institute on Drug Abuse (NIDA) found lasting cognitive deficits in those who started to smoke marijuana before age 17. The researchers analysed neuro-psychological test results from 122 long-term heavy users of marijuana and 87 subjects who had used marijuana only a few times (control subjects). Sixty-nine of the 122 users started using marijuana at age 17 or before. The subjects were between the ages of 30 and 55 at the time of the study, and all had refrained from any drug use 28 days before testing.

Individuals who started using marijuana at age 17 or younger performed significantly worse on the tests assessing verbal functions such as verbal IQ and memory of word lists than did those who started using marijuana later in life or who had used the drug sparingly. There were virtually no differences in test results among the individuals who started marijuana use after age 17, and the control subjects.

Youths who use marijuana before their mid-teens may show long-term deficits in certain verbal skills but the reasons for these deficits are not yet clear.

(Dr. Harrison Pope and colleagues published the study in
the March 2003 issue of the journal Drug and Alcohol Dependence)

Professor Robin Murray said at a conference of the Royal College of Psychiatrists in Edinburgh in June 2003, that cannabis users are seven times more likely to develop mental illnesses (than non-users) and that the drug is already one of the leading causes of psychoses in the UK.

Other research has demonstrated that the following mental disorders/illnesses can be caused, precipitated from a latent state or exacerbated by cannabis use: ~

- Development of dependence;
- Delirium (acute confusional states);
- Cannabis psychoses;
- Schizophrenia;
- Other psychoses;
- Anxiety disorders;
- Depersonalisation syndrome;
- Depression;
- Suicide;
- Amotivational syndrome; and
- Impulsively violent behaviour. (Ramstrom page 25)

As a 'rule of thumb' on average a person who smokes cannabis runs a 10‰ risk of being affected at sometime by cannabis psychosis or delirium (Ramstrom).

Lundqvist, a Swedish researcher has claimed that he is able to distinguish a typical personality profile characteristic of cannabis smoking clients. He based his opinions on extensive research with 400 chronic cannabis users and according to his profile, abusers typically:

- have difficulty in finding words to express what they really mean;
- have a limited ability to be amused by or enjoy literature, film, theatre and the like;
- have a felling of boredom and emptiness in everyday life, along with feelings of loneliness and of not being understood;
- externalise problems and are unable to take criticism;
- are convinced that they are functioning adequately;
- are unable to examine their own behaviour self-critically;

- feel that they have low capacity and are unsuccessful;

- are unable to carry on a dialogue;

- experience difficulty in concentrating and paying attention;

- have rigid (fixed) opinions and answers to questions;

- make statements such as "I'm different, other people don't understand me, I don't belong to society";

- do not plan their day;

- think they are active because they have many on-going projects
  – which are seldom seen through to completion;

- have no daily or weekly routines.

(LUNDQVIST. T Cognitive Dysfunctions in Chronic Cannabis Users 1995).

Obviously such personality traits are dependent both upon the size and strength of the dose and the duration of the abuse. The symptoms identified above have similarities to the "amotivational syndrome".

On a narrower group than the general population, of which Professor Murray was speaking, Professor Helene Verdoux of Bordeaux University said she had found that for families with a history of mental illness as few as two joints a week could trigger psychosis.

Research published in 2003 indicated an important connection between early use of cannabis and later dependency; 20% of the study group used cannabis before age 16, of that group, 21•7 percent met criteria for cannabis dependence by the age of 21. Those reporting 5 early positive responses to cannabis were 28•5 times more likely to have cannabis dependence. Early use and positive experiences in early use increase the risk for cannabis dependence.

(Fergusson DM, Horwood LJ, Lynskey MT, Madden PAF.
Early reactions to cannabis predict later dependence - Arch Gen Psychiatry 2003;60:1033-1039).

After a review of the research the federal Drug Czar in the USA announced in May 2005 that whilst the rate of mental illness is about 8-9% among US adults, the rate is 12% amongst those who use marijuana. In the case of those who use it before the age of 12 years the mental illness prevalence rises to 21% (CNN 3.5.05). The data cited came from the National Survey of Drug Use and Health, a study of twins published in the Archives of General Psychiatry, and other sources.

A report in the online journal "Nature Medicine" in May 2005 indicated that one of the UK's leading experts in osteoporosis - Professor Stuart Ralston of Edinburgh University (formerly of Aberdeen University where the research was conducted), had found a link between the heavy use of cannabis and the stimulation of bone absorbing cells that could enhance the risk of developing osteoporosis and brittle bones. Professor Ralston noted that many of the patients he has seen with brittle bone disease have been heavy drug users.

NB – for a review of the recent literature on Cannabis see also "Adverse Consequences of Cannabis Use: A Survey of Scientific Studies Published up to and including the Autumn of 2003" by Jan Ramstrom – National Institute of Public Health – Sweden, and "Cannabis as a risk factor for psychosis: systematic review" by SEMPLE David M, University of Edinburgh et al in Journal of Psychopharmcology. 19(2) (2005) 187-194.

Cannabis and Pregnancy:

There is a known risk for the babies of women who smoke cannabis during pregnancy and researchers at the Vanderbilt Medical Centre of the University of Tennessee have produced some evidence that cannabinoids may be responsible for some spontaneous abortions (BBC 25.11.03). There is also the possibility that the use of cannabis may cause premature birth. Babies born to women who use cannabis have been found to be smaller than average; they feed and settle less well. They have been noted long-term to suffer a lower attention span, increased anger and to be more socially disruptive. There is the possibility which has not been fully reported of a condition similar to foetal alcohol syndrome, which is believed to become apparent in some infants after the age of three. Cannabis may also increase the risk of minor birth defects and there is a small risk of abortion. There seems to be an increased risk of sudden infant death syndrome and there are reports that cannabis use is associated with certain forms of childhood cancers. Additionally, there is concern that cannabis smoking by a pregnant mother has an adverse effect on the child's central nervous system – (Ramstrom).

Early in 2004 a report indicated the likelihood that children of mothers who had smoked cannabis during pregnancy were likely to suffer from attention deficit disorder.

(Dr. Peter A. Fried, Barbara Watkinson Department. of Psychology, Carleton University, Ontario, Canada A Follow-up Study of Attentional Behavior in Children Exposed Prenatally to Marijuana, Cigarettes, and Alcohol).

THC can be passed to the baby through breast milk and may cause the baby to become quite unsettled and demand frequent feeding. Using cannabis while breast-feeding may delay a baby's developmental progress (crawling and walking, holding objects, coordination).

Cannabis Dependence:

Cannabis dependence is now recognised as an established phenomenon for which people may need to seek medical help (ACMD 2002; National Alcohol and Drug Addiction Centre Report [Australia] - Dr Jennifer Swift 1999). Studies amongst dependent users have revealed that when they stop they experience physical withdrawal characterised by loss of appetite and weight, lethargy, irritability, mood changes and insomnia. There is also a psychological craving for cannabis.

Research published in October 2000 by the National Institute on Drug Abuse (NIDA) in the USA has demonstrated that cannabis is as addictive as cocaine or heroin.

The American Psychiatric Association has listed the harmful effects of cannabis in the Diagnostic and Statistical Manual of Mental Disorders (DSM IV, May 1994). These include psychotic disorder (insanity), hallucinations, anxiety disorder (panic attacks), impaired judgement, sensation of slowed time, social withdrawal, perceptual disturbances, impaired motor co-ordination, delirium, memory deficit, depersonalisation, delusions, especially of persecution (paranoia), disorientation and others. These psychiatric symptoms are the cause of numerous admissions to hospital emergency rooms in the USA.

Research published in the USA has indicated that marijuana use by young people has been associated with a wide range of dangerous and anti-social behaviour. Children who begin smoking pot at an early age have been found to be statistically less likely to complete their schooling and more inclined to indulge in acts of theft, violence, vandalism and other high-risk behaviour when compared with those who do not smoke the drug. (Substance Abuse & Mental Health Services Administration, Office of Applied Studies, Analysis of Substance Abuse and Treatment Need Issues, Analytic Series A-7, DHHS Publication No SMA98-3227.

(Rockville, MD: US Dept of Health and Human Services, 1998), p93;
The Risks for Late Adolescents of Early Adolescent Marijuana Use",
American Journal of Public Health, 1549-1554,199).

Cannabis as a "gateway" to other drug use:

The "gateway" or "stepping stones" theory is controversial. Although no physiological link has been firmly established between cannabis use and the progression to the so-called hard drugs, there is evidence to show that a very significant number of those who use heroin and other 'hard' drugs began their drug using careers with cannabis. Research conducted in Sweden by Professor Yasmin Hurd, of the Karolinska Institute has shown that chronic periodic use of cannabis can interfere with the brain development.

Professor Hurd's experiments have shown that after training to self administer heroin by pushing a lever, rats exposed to THC took more heroin as adults than those that had not been given this chemical. They were more sensitive to lower doses of heroin than unexposed rats and took more to alleviate stress. If confirmed, the findings suggest that children and young adults who use the drug over long periods would be more prone to anxiety and more dependent on anxiety-reducing drugs in later life (The Daily Telegraph 18.06.05). In May 2006 Professor Hurd and her team, having moved to the Mount Sinai School of Medicine in New York, claimed that the link between early cannabis use and later opiate us had been established because the adolescent brain is particularly sensitive to drug exposure with cell changes in areas of the brain essential for behavioural functions.

(Neuropsychopharmacology – online Journal 5th July 2006).

There is also evidence of psychological dependency on all drugs, which might indicate a propensity to progress to more dangerous drugs in pursuit of greater satisfaction. Certainly a greater tolerance and acceptance of the drug culture, particularly amongst young people, has developed to such an extent that many now believe that taking drugs recreationally is 'normal'. In this respect, it is likely that a progression from cannabis smoking to the taking of Ecstasy and amphetamine type substances is seen to be both convenient and acceptable.

Proving the assertion that cannabis is a "gateway" drug is difficult because of other factors which might also act as "gateways" such as tobacco and alcohol. Other important considerations are the personality and the environment of the user. The report by ACMD (March 2002) suggests that even if the theory is correct it is likely that cannabis provides only a very small "gateway" as the majority of cannabis users never progress to the abuse of hard drugs. Nevertheless, it is also true that there have been few studies which have attempted to prove the accuracy of the "gateway" theory by correcting for other variable factors.

The ACMD report concludes that it is likely that cannabis use (and that of alcohol and tobacco) does have an effect on later Class A drug use and that in a small percentage of the population, progression to hard drug use results from previous exposure to cannabis. The report does not make clear whether it is referring to the cannabis using population or to the population as a whole. It goes on to point out a number of reasons why the use of cannabis and progression to other drug use may occur, the most important of which is that there is no separation between the cannabis and other drug markets. A cannabis dealer is likely to make available other drugs and in some cases there are reports that dealers have laced cannabis with other substances to encourage the use of 'hard' drugs.

Evidence of a study in New Zealand tracking 1200 people from birth to 21 years that found that those people who smoked a joint more than 50 times in a year were 60 times more likely to move on to harder drugs. The former UK Anti-Drug Co-ordinator said this study had convinced him that cannabis is a "gateway" drug (8.11.00 The Times).

Although no physiological link has been established between cannabis and the so called "hard" drugs, there is sufficient evidence to show that a very significant number of those who use heroin began their drug using careers through the "gateway" of cannabis and there is evidence of "psychological dependency". Not only is there new evidence which points to dependency on the most potent THC bearing products, particularly Nederweit, where 'cannabis psychosis' is widely reported, but also the tolerant attitudes among young people towards the use of 'mind-altering' substances, has increased significantly.

Since 1987, Ecstasy production has mushroomed in Holland and most of the tablets currently on sale throughout Europe and North America have been produced there. However, there were reports from the National Criminal Intelligence Service in 2003 that the UK was catching up in terms of the number of illicit laboratories being detected - particularly in Wales. Young people throughout Europe are increasingly abusing the substance and certainly, it appears that cannabis has become a "gateway" to ecstasy by virtue of the tolerance and acceptance of "soft" and "recreational" drugs that has developed in Holland during the last 30 years. Cannabis is much more dangerous now than people first realised.

The increased availability of cannabis in Europe combined with a greater tolerance of cannabis abuse has resulted in a much larger market for the substance. Unfortunately, there is overwhelming evidence that many young people throughout Europe have come to regard cannabis as a relatively harmless substance.

A survey published in April 1999 showed that one third of secondary school pupils in France had experimented with cannabis (the figure for Paris was more than 40%) and of those who had experimented with cannabis more than 50% went on to become regular abusers. A similar study in the UK revealed that 25% of 13 year olds had taken an illegal substance (in most cases, cannabis) while a study in Germany showed that 69% of juveniles attending "techno-parties" had taken cannabis. In Switzerland, the number of 15-year old pupils who have taken cannabis had quadrupled in the 12 years to 1999.

The International Narcotics Control Board issued a warning in February 2000 that all Governments should continue to emphasise the dangers of cannabis abuse and take positive steps to prevent the development of permissive attitudes towards its use. This warning stressed particularly that the THC content was getting stronger (INCB Annual Report 1999). In these circumstances it seemed perverse that the UK Anti-Drug Co-ordinator should have urged law enforcement agencies to make so-called hard drugs their priority, over cannabis.

The House of Commons Select Committee on Home Affairs conducted an enquiry into the possibility of the decriminalisation of drugs from September 2001 and its report was issued in May 2002. One of the most notable recommendations was that cannabis should be re-classified from Class B to Class C under the Misuse of Drugs Act 1971. However, the report pointed out that cannabis is a dangerous and harmful substance.

In March 2002 the Advisory Council on the Misuse of Drugs issued a report - "The classification of cannabis under the Misuse of Drugs Act 1971" which was widely misrepresented in the media. One of its most important conclusions was that further research, coupled with a public health education programme, is required. Ominously the report states "Since cannabis use has only been commonplace in the past 30 years there may be worse news to come".

The ACMD report concluded that cannabis should be reclassified from Class B to Class C because although it is a harmful substance which poses risks both to individual health and society, nevertheless its juxtaposition with the more harmful Class B drugs erroneously (and dangerously) suggests that their effects are equivalent. This has lead to the belief amongst cannabis users, that if they have had no harmful effects from cannabis then other Class B substances will be equally 'safe'. Unfortunately, little emphasis on the declaration that cannabis is a harmful substance was reported and many articles in the media concluded that reclassification equates with semi-official consent to use the drug in a similar way to alcohol and tobacco products. On 29th January 2004 the Home Secretary approved the reclassification of cannabis as a Class C drug. This gave rise to the widespread belief that cannabis is a relatively benign substance, however early in 2006 Charles Clarke the Home Secretary was reported as declaring his concern that the Government had misled the public about the possible dangers of using cannabis. He announced that it was necessary to inform the public better about cannabis and that he would enhance the education programme about that particular drug although he had not been persuaded to reclassify cannabis to a Class B drug. (The Guardian 5 January 2006, Times Online 5.1.06 BBC News 19.01.06). The ACMD reported further on cannabis after the matter had once more been referred to it and said early in 2006: "the Advisory Council remains of the view that cannabis is harmful and its consumption can lead to a wide range of physical and psychological hazards. Nevertheless, it does not recommend that the classification of cannabis products should be changed on the basis of the results of recent research into the effects on the development of mental illness. Although cannabis is unquestionably harmful, its harmfulness does not equate to that of other Class B substances either at the level of the individual or of society." Nevertheless, The Home Secretary declared that he would review the way in which drugs are classified as he was of the opinion that the categorization under the 1971 Act may be in need of amendment. The actions of the Home Secretary over this matter were implicitly criticised in 2006 by Antonio Maria Costa

What has become clear from American research is the fact that if a person does not use drugs, tobacco or alcohol before the age of 21 years then it is likely that such use will not occur in later life. However, the 'take-up' rate of smoking cigarettes is assessed to be 50%, which means that one out of every two smokers will adopt a permanent habit.

Cannabis as a Medicine.

For many years, there have been claims and anecdotal evidence that smoking cannabis has produced benefits for sufferers of various maladies. The US Office of National Drug Control Policy commissioned research by the National Academy of Science, Institute of Medicine, to review the scientific record of marijuana. A report was published early in 1999, which concluded that some of the compounds found in the substance do have a potential as a medicine in the relief of symptoms such as pain, nausea and vomiting and poor appetite associated with the wasting diseases of AIDS and cancer. In general terms, the report concluded, "marijuana (cannabis) is not a modern medicine".

(See "Marijuana as Medicine - The Science beyond the Controversy"
by Alison Mack and Janet Joy, National Academy Press 2001
- written by the Report researchers).

This report demonstrated that for most sufferers, there are other, more effective drugs available, but for the few who do not respond to standard medications there is the possibility that new drugs could be developed from cannabinoids, which may be efficacious.

Under no circumstances would it be normal for the drug to be ingested by smoking the cannabis, not only because of the dangers inherent in that method but also because smoke is an unsatisfactory and uncontrolled delivery system. Smoking a crude substance raises difficulties in standardising doses, assuring purity and because of the toxins and contaminants in cannabis. No substance has yet received approval for medicinal use that involves smoking.

The only circumstances in which it was thought likely that smoking cannabis might be considered for medical purposes would be for short-term use (less than 6 months) for patients with debilitating symptoms or in the case of the terminally ill. Even in these unusual circumstances, the researchers concluded that patients who are prescribed marijuana should be subjected to clinical trials, approved and overseen by proper medical review involving selected patients most likely to benefit.

Such patients should be fully aware of the nature of the trials and fully cognisant of the risks involved. These experiments should be used as a means of developing safe delivery systems from proven beneficial cannabinoids. The eventual approval of the use of cannabinoids should be subject to the same procedures for the adoption of any other drug.

The researchers did not support the use of cannabis for glaucoma, multiple sclerosis, or any other chronic condition. In the case of glaucoma, this view was endorsed in November 1999 by research published in The Lancet by Professor Anne Coleman, which indicated that the amount of marijuana necessary to be smoked to produce any clinical benefits may be associated with substantial and negative side-effects. Thus, its use could not be recommended as a treatment for glaucoma.

The US Federal Government has said that it endorses the therapeutic use of any substance which meets strict standards of safety and effectiveness based upon scientific merit. Both Federal law and International Treaties oppose the legalisation of drugs of abuse. Cannabis has been recognised as a drug of abuse and its increased potency over the last two decades has made it the leading cause of drug-related emergency room episodes in the USA.

Both the Institute of Medicine and the American Medical Association have expressed serious doubts about smoking and have stated that any research into the medicinal use of cannabis must be aimed at securing benefits from pure or synthetic cannabinoids. (See "Cannabis sativa as a Medical Application: The Need to Distinguish between Isolated Cannabinoids and Smoked Marijuana", Kevin A. Sabet 'Addictions' 1999).

The researchers recognised the problems associated with slow acting Marinol THC capsules and recommended clinical trials for the development of an inhaler or aerosol, which could be used as a rapid delivery system of precise doses of approved and licensed medicines, without the associated danger of smoking. There is too the possibility that THC could be delivered by way of sublingual preparations, nasal sprays, suppositories, or even by transdermal patches.

It was reported (Sunday Telegraph 13.6.99) that an experimental inhaler, similar to those used by sufferers of asthma was ready to go on trial in the UK in July 1999 for a period of 3 years involving 900 patients. These trials were subject to approval by the Medicines Control Agency. It was the stated intention of the manufacturers to produce the beneficial effects of cannabis without replicating the dangers associated with tobacco smoking.

In March 2000 a report appeared in the journal "Nature" by David Baker of the Institute of Neurology in London, and Dr Lorna Laywood of the Multiple Sclerosis Society, and indicated that trials on mice with MS type symptoms showed that cannabinoid extracts did alleviate the disabling effects. Their research also used cannabinoid related synthetic drugs. This gave rise to the claim that similar results might be achieved in human patients. However, research published by UCLA's Jonsson Cancer Center found that THC limits immune response and can produce tumour growth.

(Journal of Immunology, July 2000)

In a report published in a scientific journal (Movement Disorders, Vol. 17, No. 1, 2002), Fox and associates from the United Kingdom, reported on their "Randomised, double-blind, Placebo-Controlled" crossover study designed to see whether Nabilone would be effective in the treatment of muscle spasm (dystonia) associated with multiple sclerosis. The results of the study "showed no significant reduction in dystonia following treatment with Nabilone".

Though the researchers seemed to have expected more favourable results they were consistent with a controlled, double-blind study done in 1995 on balance and co-ordination of MS patients using smoked marijuana. Although the participants claimed to have relief from symptoms, high tech monitoring equipment showed that smoking marijuana actually made matters worse.

A report from researchers at Imperial College, London (July 2000 edition of Molecular and Cellular Neuroscience) found evidence that cannabinoids act on the spinal cord as well as the brain. This gave rise to the theory that drugs derived from cannabinoids could be used to target the spinal cord to dampen pain without affecting the brain and causing the euphoric high associated with cannabis. However, an article in the British Medical Journal (NO 323/2001) by F.A.Campbell concluded that cannabinoids are no more effective at controlling pain than codeine and their depressant effects limit their usefulness. They should not be used in the treatment of acute pain and their widespread introduction for the clinical treatment of pain was said to be undesirable.

Researchers from the University Hospital in Helsinki found that cannabis is no better than codeine in controlling pain and that a series of undesirable side-effects mean that it has no place at present in mainstream medicine and there are better alternatives.

(Professor Eija Kalso).

This finding was endorsed, by the Pain Management Centre at Queen's Medical Centre, Nottingham University and in an article in the British Medical Journal (July 2001) which reported on a review of 39 clinical studies which indicated that cannabis is not "a neglected wonder drug".

In The Netherlands, cannabis was not recognised as a medicine until September 2003 when it was permitted for doctors to prescribe it for chronically ill patients. In the UK the British Medical Association recommended that "certain additional cannabinoids should be legalised for wider medical use". The BMA Report entitled "The Therapeutic Use of Cannabis" (18.11.97) concluded that cannabis itself is unsuitable for medical use.

At its Annual Conference in Belfast in 1999, the British Medical Association voted overwhelmingly against the use of cannabis as a recreational drug. (The Times 8.7.99)

In 1999 the UK Government authorised licensed growing of cannabis crops for scientific research purposes and in December of that year the Medical Research Council announced a three year experiment involving 600 patients to test the efficacy of cannabis/extracts in the treatment of multiple sclerosis.

In July 2001, the Canadian Government authorised the use of marijuana for use by patients with a terminally ill or chronic condition. Regulations allow those who are granted permission to use the drug to grow a maximum of seven plants at home, or to designate others to supply them. The rules permit drug possession for the terminally ill with a prognosis of death within one year. Patients with a number of serious medical conditions and those with other conditions, who have statements from two doctors saying conventional treatments have not worked, are also permitted to grow their own supplies or to designate others to supply it for them. Eligible patients include those with severe arthritis, cancer, HIV-AIDS, and multiple sclerosis.

The Canadian Medical Association opposed the new regulations because they make doctors responsible for prescribing a drug which, it claims, lacks significant clinical research into its effects. In 2003 the High Court ruled that doctors must be provided with small amounts of cannabis for prescription purposes. This is the subject of heated debate and criticism, not least because the supplied cannabis ages and loses any potency.

In May 2004 the pharmaceutical giant Bayer Health Care applied to market marijuana based drugs in Canada for the relief of pain associated with multiple sclerosis and neuropathic pain. Bayer and GW Pharmaceutical of Great Britain filed a submission to Health Canada for the oral spray Sativex to be licensed and this was approved in 2006. British authorities rejected the drug on the grounds that there was insufficient evidence to show that the risk-benefit relationship was favourable. The Medicines and Healthcare Products Regulatory Authority announced in June 2005 that the licence application to treat spasticity (for multiple sclerosis sufferers) filed by GW Pharmaceuticals, which designed and manufactured Sativex, had been turned down on appeal. The MHRA was satisfied that the drug was safe and of good quality but that it failed on the grounds of efficacy (The Guardian 11.06.05).However, it was reported in November 2005 that the Home Office had agreed that the drug could be used under certain exceptional circumstances by special application of a doctor for the treatment of multiple sclerosis and rheumatoid arthritis (The Guardian 17.11.05). Nevertheless, a Coroner held in December 2005 that Sativex was "a significant contributory factor" in the failing health of a pensioner and the illness that eventually killed her. The patient had been prescribed Sativex to ease pain and numbness of the limbs caused by an extreme form of diabetes. Only hours after taking Sativex the patient developed disturbed behaviour to the extent that she was later admitted to hospital in "a confused and intoxicated state"; she died five months later from kidney failure. (The Times 17.12.05)

The Annual Report of the International Narcotics Control Board (INCB) in 1998 stressed that medical research should not become a pretext for legalising cannabis. The Report concluded: "Political initiatives and public votes can easily be misused by groups promoting the legalisation of cannabis for recreational use under the guise of medical dispensation".

There is little doubt that some people have used the excuse of medical benefits as a device to gain public sympathy towards the legalisation of cannabis and other drugs. As long ago as 1979 it was reported that a former director of NORML, (National Organisation for the Reform of Marijuana Laws) said - "We will use the medical marijuana argument as a red herring to give pot a good name". (Policing Today Feb. 1995)

Part of the anecdotal support associated with the alleged beneficial effects of cannabis are that it is said to reduce eye pressure in glaucoma, help spasticity in cases of multiple sclerosis, benefit pain syndrome, reduce nausea associated with chemotherapy, reduce depression, help migraine sufferers and reduce menstrual cramps. Those in favour of the legalisation of cannabis are accused of using the alleged benefits as a "Trojan Horse" in the concealment of their real intentions.

Most of the claims about medical benefits of cannabis have yet to be backed up by scientific evidence, but there is hope that cannabinoids may be refined to produce useful drugs in the future. To date cannabis has not been subjected to the rigorous tests necessary to prove its efficacy and safety as a medicine as required by law on both sides of the Atlantic. Marijuana is an intoxicating substance and so there is little surprise that sincere people have reported relief of their symptoms when they smoke it. The important point to consider is that there is a difference between feeling better and actually getting better.

In August 2003, the Medical Research Council in the UK announced controversial trials to see whether cannabis can relieve the pain of patients who have undergone surgery. The trial is to use 400 patients at 36 different hospitals throughout Britain and will use a capsule with a standardised extract of the entire cannabis plant. (The Guardian 21.8.03)

There is evidence that in the states of California and Arizona, voters were misled into supporting the medical use of marijuana by a well-financed campaign that was more to do with the legalisation of cannabis than it was with concern about the treatment of patients.

Clearly, the question of medication is a matter for scientific assessment and should not be left to the misinformed opinions of a confused electorate. Several other US States have passed laws which allow the use of marijuana as a form of medical treatment and that is subject to legal challenges to prevent the indiscriminate use of marijuana under the guise of medical approval. Federal laws do not recognise the concept of medical marijuana.

In an effort to combat the fraudulent misuse of cannabis, several American cities have introduced laws to require patients to carry "medical marijuana identification cards" to protect them from prosecution under State law.

In San Francisco, the law made allowance for the provision of identification cards valid for two years at a cost of $25. Patients who possessed such cards were permitted to obtain cannabis for medical purposes only from any of several marijuana buyers' co-operatives in the San Francisco Bay area. However, on 14th May 2001 the US Supreme Court held: -

"There is no medical necessity exception to the Controlled Substances Act's prohibition on manufacturing and distributing marijuana".

This ruling effectively put an end to the arguments used in California to support the use of marijuana as a form of self-medication although the State Supreme Court continued to uphold the use of marijuana for medicinal purposes thus creating a conflict between State and Federal law.

In June of 2005 the US Supreme Court ruled against medical marijuana and held in Gonzales v Raich that Federal Authorities may prosecute sick people who smoke pot on a doctor's orders. It held that State laws do not protect users from a Federal ban on the drug.

There should be no doubt that cannabis is a proven addictive and potentially very dangerous drug. The most likely outcome from research into cannabis is that scientists may be motivated to develop some more useful synthetic medicines and they may come better to understand the function of cannabinoids produced naturally in the human body. It is known already that cannabinoids influence physiology and biochemistry and this area of research could result in some new and highly specific drugs derived artificially and not from plants.

The medical future of the cannabis plant probably seems very limited and the current debate and expectations are likely, eventually to fade into the mists of time. There is absolutely no scientific evidence to date to indicate that smoking cannabis provides some sort of "silver bullet" that will offer miracle cures in the future and we should not be misled by false arguments and media hype which suggests the contrary.

In September 2003 the Dutch Government authorised the prescription of cannabis while at the same time acknowledging the lack of evidence that it is efficacious. Most doctors in the country have acknowledged the mental health risks involved with the prolonged use of cannabis.

In November 2005 The Royal College of Physicians issued a Report of a Working Party that had examined the possibility of further research into cannabis and cannabis based medicines. It stressed the importance of distinguishing between cannabis and the use of cannabis based medicines but concluded that further research would be desirable and mentioned existing research projects associated with the use of cannabinoids.

(Cannabis and Cannabis –based medicines.
Potential benefits and risks to health, Report of a Working Party - 2005)

Tolerance of any drug can be dangerous.

It appears that the Dutch came to realise the dangers of an excessively liberal and tolerant stance on drug abuse. Evidence has shown a dangerous and excessive use of cannabis and ecstasy resulting in dependency and harm, and increased use of "hard" drugs and associated criminal conduct.

(see "Half-baked Drug Experiment" – Foreign Affairs, May/June 1999 by Larry Collins; see also
"Dazed and Confused, Smoke and Mirrors over Dutch Drug Policy" Foreign Affairs Nov/Dec.1999;
'Coffee Shops Geteld' Coffee Shops and other points of sale. Hassela Nordic Network.).

In April 1998, the U.K. government published a ten-year, strategy for tackling the drug problem. Shortly after that document was released, it was reported that the U.K. Anti-Drug Co-ordinator had asked HM Customs & Excise to prioritise Class A drugs, (e.g.

heroin, cocaine), in their efforts to enforce the law and to interdict illicit supplies. This meant that with their limited resources the Customs were to give less attention to the so-called "soft" drugs like cannabis and ecstasy.

Again in February 2000 the UK Anti-Drug Co-ordinator stated that, in his opinion the police and customs should concentrate their enforcement activities against the so-called 'hard drugs'. He stated that he did not approve of legalising cannabis but had made his remarks because priorities have to be made and he considers that the hard drugs cause the most damage to society.

(BBC News 6.2.00, "Frost on Sunday" Interview BBC1 13.02.00)

While it is understandable that priorities have to be made, there is the distinct danger that any failure fully to address the cannabis problem will send the wrong message to many people who have already inclined to the view that cannabis is not a dangerous drug. If the government enforcement initiative does not give a high priority to cannabis interdiction combined with the recommended public health education programme, the inference will be drawn, as occurred in Holland and elsewhere, that it cannot be a particularly harmful substance. Already a culture of tolerance and acceptance in the U.K. has given rise to a widespread belief that cannabis is safe and should be legalised.

In March 2000 the Police Foundation (not a police organisation) Report was published. It received attention because of its recommendations that cannabis should be transferred from Class B to Class C of schedule 2 of the Misuse of Drugs Act 1971, and that cannabinol and its derivatives should be transferred from Class A to Class C of that schedule. The report recommended that the possession of cannabis should not be an imprisonable offence, and that possession of cannabis should not be an arrestable offence in England and Wales.

Although the Home Affairs Select Committee Report in 2002, on government drug policy did not support the legalisation of any drug, it did recommend the reclassification of cannabis into the lowest category of dangerous drugs. In the opinion of many people, this lent support to the widely held view that cannabis is not a particularly harmful drug.

The U.K. has one of the worst records in Europe with the misuse of drugs and the resulting dependency and it is likely that failure to control the importation of cannabis can only result in an increased danger to many individuals and society.

Annexe to Chapter on Cannabis.
International experiences with legalisation: Holland.

For over 25 years, the use of cannabis has been tolerated under Dutch law in very restricted circumstances. In 1976, the Dutch Parliament accepted recommendations made in the Baan Commission Report that a distinction should be made between drugs that presented an unacceptable risk, such as heroin, cocaine and LSD, and the less dangerous, or "soft" drugs like marijuana. Possession of 30grams of marijuana was permitted for adult, personal use and "cannabis cafes" or licensed coffee shops (over 400 in Amsterdam) were established, in which it was permissible to sell up to 30grams to adults. Hard drugs remained subject to prohibition.

Although the Dutch experience has been held out to be a successful and enlightened approach to the problem of drugs, intended to de-mystify cannabis and to prevent a progression to harder and addictive drugs, the reality has proved to be a very damaging opposite of that intention. In 1996, the Dutch Minister of Justice acknowledged that Holland had become the "crime capital of Europe", with thefts, vandalism, firearms offences and addictions to hard drugs escalating to very high levels.

Many people had come to accept the link between these increases and the liberal attitudes towards cannabis. From 1987 Holland had also become the major European production source of Ecstasy tablets and an associated attitude of tolerance and acceptance of these, so called "soft" drugs had become common amongst the younger generation, both in Holland and throughout the rest of Europe.

It has been claimed that the tolerant attitude towards drugs has now permeated all levels of officialdom in Holland, particularly within the Criminal Justice System, because those presently in policy influencing positions have grown up in the post Baan era.

International experts in drugs and law enforcement have come to agree that cannabis has become more potent since 1976, to such an extent that it is a totally different substance to that which was officially approved by Baan.

(International Narcotics Control Board Annual Report 1999)

Cannabis has now a proven record of dependency and Dutch officials across the social spectrum have come to realise that the effective decriminalisation of cannabis has had unforeseen and devastating consequences.

(see "Holland's Half Baked Drug Experiment" – Foreign Affairs May/June 1999 Vol. 78 No.3; see also Dazed and Confused Smoke and Mirrors over Dutch Drug Policy Foreign Affairs Nov/Dec 1999).

In 1995 the Dutch government ordered a reduction in the number of licensed coffee shops, cutting the number from 400 to just 65 in Amsterdam, and at the same time they reduced the quantity of cannabis that could be sold legally, from 30grams per adult to 5grams. Police welcomed the government action and to many people it was a belated recognition that the original policy had been seriously wrong and had caused irretrievable harm. In May 2004 the Dutch Government expressed it concern about the high THC content of cannabis plants and moved top prevent drug tourism.

Sadly, the Dutch experiment is still widely regarded as being successful by those who seek the wholesale, legalisation of cannabis. Even in the face of irrefutable evidence that such a measure is desirable, the Dutch government of the day lacked the courage to re-introduce a total ban on the substance for personal consumption. However, a new government elected in 2002 indicated that it would take steps to change the policy of tolerance towards cannabis. In 2003 there was a move which will affect the ability of the cannabis cafes to permit smoking on their premises.

An article in De Volkskrant Netherlands (The Week 22.4.00) draws attention to the widespread opinion in Holland that the majority of people no longer wish to go along with that country's laissez faire attitude to the consumption of drugs. 'All country, citizens' action groups' were formed to draw attention to the harm that has been caused by the 'tolerance' towards drug users. These groups pointed out, that each drug addict that comes to the attention of the police is responsible on average, for 135 crimes a year, mostly theft. A former police chief in Rotterdam is quoted as saying – "We have ended up not knowing exactly what is tolerated. Indeed, these days, we are in effect tolerating organised crime".

However, in 2001 the town of Venlo, one mile from the German border, authorised two "drive-thru" cafes licensed to sell cannabis. This action was to cope with the large number of customers who travel from Germany in order to purchase the drug and put great pressure on the town. The Dutch newspapers have nicknamed these cafes "McDope". (The Guardian 1.6.01)

On 1st March 2003, the Dutch Government permitted doctors to prescribe cannabis cases and in September 2003 the Government authorised the prescription of cannabis but retained the right of supply.

As of 14th February 2006 Twelve states in the USA — Alaska, Arizona, California, Colorado, Hawaii, Maine, Montana, Nevada, Oregon, Rhode Island, Vermont, and Washington—have enacted laws allowing the use of marijuana for 'medical' purposes with a doctor's recommendation or prescription.

Alaska

In 1975, the Supreme Court in Alaska decriminalised the personal possession of cannabis in the home or other private places, almost by accident. (Ravin v Alaska)

A lawyer named Irwin Ravin had been arrested in 1972 for the possession of cannabis while driving his car. Ravin challenged the case on grounds that the State had not demonstrated a compelling government interest in outlawing the personal possession of marijuana. The result of this argument was that the court extended the constitutional right to privacy to allow possession of "small, personal amounts" of the substance, which in 1982, was officially defined as 4ozs.

Research by the Center for Alcohol and Addiction Studies at the University of Alaska in 1988, indicated that after this effective decriminalisation of the possession of cannabis by adults, use by minors was twice as high as the average consumption in other States. For 12-17 years olds lifetime experience of marijuana was 51.6% compared with a national average for the same age group of 23.7%. The researchers concluded that, far from cannabis experimentation being part of a general adolescent experience, the use of marijuana had become deeply rooted into the habits of a significantly large number of Alaskan young people. Reported addictions increased significantly and from 1988–90 over 2000 patients were admitted to treatment programmes funded out of tax revenues. Many young people suffered the same kinds of symptoms of amotivation and increased suicides that had been noted in Holland.

The University of Mississippi reaffirmed the conclusions arrived at elsewhere about marijuana, that the increased THC potency in 1989 had made it a markedly different substance from that in use at the time of Ravin's arrest in 1972, although his arguments to the Supreme Court remained as valid. Nevertheless, a groundswell of public opinion against the continued legal possession of marijuana, backed up by the statistics, which demonstrated increased addictions, resulted in a campaign to re-criminalise marijuana. In 1990, legislation was introduced which gave effect to the public demands. The Alaskan experience of legalising marijuana had been another horror story, which eventually shocked a large number of concerned people to react against it.

Court affirms right to possess pot.

• **Ruling**: Alaskans can have a small amount of marijuana in their homes; state vows high court review.

• **Juneau:** In a ruling handed down Friday, a state appellate court has affirmed the right of Alaskans to possess a small amount of marijuana in their homes. The state

Court of Appeals, in a unanimous ruling, reversed a 2001 conviction of a North Pole man found with marijuana in his home and ordered a new trial. In striking down the conviction of David S. Noy, the court called into question a 1990 voter initiative that criminalized possession of any amount of marijuana.

(By MIKE CHAMBERS, The Associated Press Published: August 30, 2003)

In early 2004 sufficient signatures were obtained to permit a reconsideration of the legalisation of cannabis but as late as March 2006 the debate continued and no firm ruling had been applied; however, in May 2006 the Governor won approval for legislation to re-criminalize marijuana.

U.S.A.

Between 1975-8, the United States 11 States decriminalised personal possession of cannabis and made it a civil offence punishable only by way of a fine. Accurate records were not kept and it has been difficult to assess the impact that this had, although there are no indications that this resulted in increased consumption in these States compared with those who had not followed that policy.

The two most shocking examples of the so-called medicinal use of marijuana occurred in the States of California and Arizona in 1996. Despite serious warnings from the President of the USA and three of his predecessors in office, law enforcement officials, the State Governors and the Drugs Czar, voters supported Proposition 200 in Arizona and Proposition 215 in California, which allowed medical patients to use marijuana almost without restriction. In the case of Arizona, the proposition allowed doctors to recommend any drug they saw fit, including heroin, LSD, and PCP. The proposition also encouraged the immediate release of over 1000 prisoners who had been incarcerated for non-violent drug offences and recommended the prohibition on custodial sentences for such offences until the third conviction. The measures won substantial electoral approval with 56% of the voters in California and 66% in Arizona voting in favour.

There is little doubt that the voters in both States were duped into supporting the measures by unsubstantiated and anecdotal stories about the medicinal benefits of marijuana broadcast in the media and financed, in large measure by out of State supporters of the legalisation of drugs. Not surprisingly, there was a public reaction against the legislation once the deception had become widely recognised. A public opinion survey conducted by the University of Arizona claims to demonstrate that 85% of registered voters believe that Proposition 200 should be amended because of the unintended and dangerous consequences, and that 60% of registered voters believe that it should be repealed. A bill was introduced in the State legislature to limit medical marijuana recommendations only to California registered physicians. The prescriptions must be in writing and can only relate to adult patients of the age of 18 and over.

In 1998, there were 22 States, which had enabling legislation permitting some form of research into the medicinal use of marijuana; by 1999 eight States had voted for the medicinal use of marijuana.

CHAPTER 6
Specific Drugs.

UK law puts drugs into three separate classes A, B and C - according to the assessed harm that they can do to users.

Class A includes cocaine, crack, ecstasy, heroin, LSD, and hallucinogenic or "magic" mushrooms (Crystal Meth is to be included in this category following a Government announcement in June 2006). Penalty for possession is a maximum of 7 years imprisonment plus an unlimited fine. For supplying and dealing it is life imprisonment and an unlimited fine and possession with intent to supply carries the same penalty.

Class B includes amphetamines but any Class B substance prepared for injection is treated as Class A. Possession carries a penalty of 5 years imprisonment plus an unlimited fine. Supplying and dealing carries a maximum of 14 years jail plus an unlimited fine and possession with intent to supply carries a similar penalty.

Class C includes cannabis, GHB, anabolic (tissue building) steroids and tranquillisers such as Valium. The maximum penalty for possession is 2 years jail plus an unlimited fine; for supplying and dealing is 14 years jail with an unlimited fine and similarly for possession with intent to supply.(Cannabis was reclassified on 29.1.04 from Class B to Class C. (Misuse of Drugs Act 1971)

However, there have been concerns over many years about the validity of this classification system and it was severely criticised in July 2006 by the House of Commons Science and Technology Committee ("Drug Classification: making a hash of it?" ,HC 1031 31.07.06). The Committee found significant anomalies in the classification of individual drugs and "a regrettable lack of consistency in the rationale used to make classification decisions." Additionally, the Committee expressed concern at the Government's proclivity for the use of the system as a means of 'sending out signals' to potential users and society at large which it said was at odds with the stated objective of classifying drugs on the basis of harm. The Government was accused of failing to develop an evidence base on which to draw in determining the signal to be sent out.

More to the point the Committee expressed the view that there was no convincing evidence for the deterrent effect that is supposed to underpin the Government's classification policy. The Committee concluded that the current classification system is not fit for purpose although it did not recommend an alternative system other than to say that it believed that it should be replaced by a more scientifically based scale of harm, decoupled from penalties for possession and trafficking. The Committee urged the Home Secretary to undertake an urgent review of the system.

Clearly it would be a sensible starting point to warn the general public that all illicit drugs are dangerous and leave the courts to decide on relevant penalties according to the circumstances of each individual case.

On 13th October, 2006 the Government announced that it would not change the existing drug classification system.

Heroin

The UNODC estimated that in 2004 approximately 16 million people abused opium and heroin worldwide and more people are treated for opiates abuse than any other substance. Over 60% of drug related treatment demand in Europe and Asia is related to the abuse of opiates (World Drug Report 2005). Although there have been regional variations in production the total world output has remained more or less constant and there are worrying increases in abuse reported in Central Asia, the Russian Federation, Eastern Europe and the Baltic States where the market for Afghan heroin is growing.

Heroin is the most commonly abused drug of the opiate variety (morphine, heroin, and codeine) derived from the opium poppy (Papaver somniferum) which grows wild or is cultivated in many countries. Heroin is a semi-synthetic substance and from a health point of view, it is probably the most serious drug of abuse, with many young people turning to it for their first experience of illicit drugs. Reports by the Russian agency, Itar-Tass, have indicated that children as young as eight years of age have been registered as heroin addicts in the Tyumen Regional Centre. (Itar-Tass, World Service, 10.6.99)

Heroin is widely used and in most countries, it is a leading drug responsible for substance abuse related deaths and emergency room crises. Abuse throughout the Americas and Africa, is below average whereas in Asia, Europe and Oceania, it is above global average.

Seizures by H.M. Customs in the UK amounted to 1.7 tonnes in 1998; this amount was nearly three times more than the next biggest haul of heroin in Europe (Sunday Herald 30.5.99). However, it is small when compared with the vast amounts that are produced and exported world-wide. In 2000, the National Criminal Intelligence Service estimated that between 30-40 tonnes is entering the UK unchecked each year.

In 1999, the UNDCCP estimate of production of opium in Afghanistan was 4600 metric tons (this reduces to approx. 450 tons of heroin) twice the estimate for the previous year. An estimated 2 million addicts in Pakistan were said to consume 130 metric tons each year with the addiction rate growing 7% per annum, the equivalent of 16 new addicts per hour. Most of the heroin came from Afghanistan where local farmers were paid $60 a kilo for their poppy crop, whereas the going rate for an equivalent amount of wheat was less than a dollar (1999 prices). The farmers could not then afford to replace the poppy with wheat.

Reports emanating from Afghanistan in 1999 indicated that the Khandahar Valley was full of extensive poppy fields where once apples, grapes, and other fruits were common. The fruit orchards in this valley were once watered by a complex and well-maintained irrigation system until the Soviet invasion in 1979 when both the Soviets and the Mujaheddin mined the area so that the civilian population fled to Pakistan and the orchards were abandoned.

The Mujaheddin used the irrigation ditches and orchards as cover to attack the Soviet troops who retaliated by defoliation and the destruction of the irrigation system. When the refugees returned to this devastated area in 1990, they started to grow opium poppies for a livelihood and this became the major source of income for the Taliban. Although the Koran prohibits Muslims from producing or imbibing intoxicants, the logic is that "Opium is permissible because it is consumed by kafirs (unbelievers)". There was also the fear amongst the Taliban leaders that there would be an uprising against their rule if opium production were to be stopped.

Another political imperative was the fact that although the Taliban recognised the evil consequences of opium, they could not afford to promote alternative crop production until they secured International recognition for their Government. Indeed, this "offer" was used as a bargaining point in their quest for recognition.

Periodic undertakings were given both to the US and the UN that the Taliban would ban the crop but the reality was different and it is almost impossible to control production of such a lucrative crop in such a vast country. ("The Taliban Exporting Extremism" Ahmed Rashid Foreign Affairs Nov/Dec. 1999; "Taliban" by Ahmed Rashid, I.B.Tauris, 2000; see also International Narcotics Control Strategy Report - 1999 released by US Dept. of State). Estimates are that the Taliban obtained at least US$20 million in taxation of the ever-increasing opium crop, and many of the Warlords made a great deal more on the side. In Herat the Taliban set up model farms where farmers learned the best methods of opium poppy cultivation.

The estimated area under poppy cultivation in 1997/8 was 64000 hectares, an increase of 9% over 1996/7. In 1998/9, the International Narcotics Control Board estimated that 75% of the world's production of opium took place in Afghanistan and that some 90,000 hectares of land was under poppy cultivation; an increase of 40% on the previous season (INCB Annual Report 1999). The INCB concluded that the number of illicit laboratories for processing heroin had increased in Afghanistan, thus making nonsense of the Taliban claim that they would restrict drug production.

There is also substantial evidence that the necessary precursor chemicals for producing heroin are smuggled across the borders into Afghanistan. The heroin crops are exported by the ton through Tajikistan and neighbouring countries, Pakistan, Iran and through Turkey to Western Europe and the USA. It is thought that some of the supplies through Pakistan are shipped to Europe via East African ports and the free port of Dubai.

("New Internationalist", October,1999)

An estimate of between 60-75% of the world's heroin supply originated from Afghanistan but by the beginning of the twenty-first century that estimate was agreed to be nearer to 89%. Cannabis crops are also grown in this country. The geographical location at the gateway to Central Asia and Europe has made the former "Silk Route" a lucrative highway for drug trafficking from South and South East Asia.

(But see "Bare poppy fields sow fatal harvest" The Observer 17.6.2001)

Even after the effective overthrow of the Taliban regime in 2002 by coalition forces, there was evidence that poppy growing was thriving again and that this source of opium will continue for many years to come. Afghanistan is such a large country with long, uncontrolled borders and many of the existing warlords and tribesmen see the production of opium crops as one sure way of maintaining an income. Bumper crops were reported in the years 2003-2005 with little sign that international efforts to control the crop were meeting with much success. According to intelligence sources the terrorist group headed by Osama bin Laden - Al Q'aeda obtains much of its funding from trading in drugs, particularly from Afghanistan.

("Funding Evil; How Terrorism is financed and How to Stop It"
Rachel Ehrenfield Bonus Books 2003)

Although the two leading producers of heroin are Afghanistan and Myanmar, other countries are now growing opium poppies on a large scale to service the domestic consumption of heroin and to avoid the problems of transportation. Heroin is now produced extensively in Latin America, particularly in Colombia, and it has been reported in continental USA.

Heroin - the drug:-

Heroin is a morphine derivative and the most potent of the opiates. It is easily dissolved for injection purposes and has a more rapid entry to the brain compared with morphine; the effects last between 4-6 hours. It can be 'snorted', smoked or inhaled by heating the substance on tinfoil and then breathing in the fumes; this method is referred to as "chasing the dragon" and has given rise to the widespread misconception that heroin used in this way is not addictive.

Some people prefer inhalation as the best way of using the drug, as this method is not associated with the stigma attached to injection or the risk of infections from the use of unclean equipment. However, the result of research published in the Neurology Journal (12.11.99) indicated that the practice of heating heroin on tinfoil puts such users at greater risk of developing a potentially fatal brain disorder – 'spongiform leukoencephalopy'.

Heroin was widely used in medicines at the end of the 19th and beginning of the 20th centuries, but once its addictive properties became known its use for this purpose became less frequent. Predominantly it is now used as a drug of abuse with a very high risk that dependency may develop.

Opiates depress the central nervous system and they are used therapeutically as pain-killers (the most common type for this purpose is codeine), as a cough suppressant and for the treatment of diarrhoea. As a substance of abuse, heroin is used for a variety of emotional reasons and has even been used to "come down" from the exhilarating effects of Ecstasy.

Heroin is a powder, which varies in colour from white to dark brown, depending upon the level of impurities.

Opium is obtained by processing a white, milky fluid, which oozes from the slashed poppy seedpods in the form of sap; it is then dried and processed. Once the opium sap has been gathered, it is mixed with lime and ammonia, the formation of crude heroin occurs with the bonding of the morphine and acetic acid. Impurities are then removed from the crude substance using chloroform and water. The conversion to purer powder form is achieved using ether and hydrochloric acid in a risky procedure requiring sophisticated skills.

Nowadays, this process occurs near to the harvesting sites in much the same way as the manufacture of cocaine. Sometimes very sophisticated laboratories are used in order to increase the value of the product because of the bulk and weight associated with transporting unprocessed raw material.

Another means of obtaining opium is through the processing of the poppy straw from which alkaloids are extracted. This extract may be liquid, powder, or solid but the most common, commercial form is powder. The USA imports over 500 tons of poppy straw concentrate for legitimate, medical use; some of it is used to manufacture medication for the treatment of diarrhoea, but the majority is used for making pain-killers.

Illegal heroin consumption is on the increase world-wide and the purity levels now available are significantly higher than they were a few years ago. In the early days of widespread abuse, the substance was full of imperfections and impurities and the powder was "cut" with a variety of substances to increase the bulk, thus enabling the dealers to get greater profits. Sugars, starch flour, powdered milk, and even talcum powder were used and some of the more ruthless dealers used other harmful products in order to maximise their profits. Initial purity levels were between 1-10% but now purity levels often reach as high as 90% although 40-50% is more normal.

Heroin effects: -

The major influence of heroin is upon the central nervous system, which in turn controls the major survival functions of respiration, circulation, and digestion. Opiates reduce the rate of heartbeat thus causing a relaxation in the blood vessels and a lowering of blood pressure; this is conjoined with muscle relaxation and a slowing of the rate of both breathing and digestion.

Often a state of drowsiness is induced, although heroin is also associated with an initial state of euphoria. As with other drugs, the induced state often depends upon the attitudes of the users and the circumstances under which ingestion occurs. The "high" caused by the drug can last between 4-6 hours but frequency of use diminishes this effect, with the result that more frequent and potent "fixes" are required to obtain the same initial sensation.

Heroin is highly addictive and causes dependence. A user may build up a high tolerance to heroin very quickly but if heroin use is denied the tolerance can be lost equally quickly. The body develops both a tolerance of, and a craving for heroin. Dependency can be both physical and psychological although the horrendous descriptions of withdrawal are seldom accurate and in most cases resemble a severe bout of 'flu, sometimes associated with nausea, cold sweats, muscle spasms and cramps together with diarrhoea.

In 2005 there were suggestions from the Scottish Prison Service that it intended "re-toxifying" prisoners due for release with a course of methadone in an attempt to stop some of them from overdosing on heroin if they attempted to use the high levels that they were used to before imprisonment. Naturally, there were objections to this practice on the grounds that proper care and detoxification should occur while the prisoners were carrying out their sentences.

A significant type of dependency, in addition to the physical, is psychological. The associated rituals developed by intravenous drug users can cause a dependence on the needle as much as the drug and the camaraderie associated with sharing both drugs and the equipment necessary for heroin injections is 'infectious'.

Dependent heroin users, who are aware of the risks involved of contracting either AIDS/HIV or Hepatitis C, endocarditis and the formation of abscesses still choose to inject. They consider this method to be the most economical way of achieving the maximum effect and the complete use of available heroin; injecting directly into a major vein is called "mainlining". The principal risk of heroin overdose is respiratory depression.

Higher purity levels and the uncertainty of the potency of illegally purchased drugs encourages newer users to "snort" the powder into the nostrils, although it can be absorbed quite rapidly through the mucous membranes; others use injection under the skin referred to as "popping". Experienced users consider the latter method to be wasteful and less effective

Sometimes, abusers will use a cocktail of drugs or combine heroin with amphetamines in an attempt to get an extra "high". This very dangerous method of abuse is called "speed-balling", and has claimed the lives of many, including the American entertainer, John Belushi, who died in 1982. There has been a recent increase in the number of heroin related deaths wherever the drug is abused, but particularly in the UK. The main cause of harm is often associated with unsanitary injecting techniques or overdosing, although others have died, because of the use of a cocktail of drugs. Impurities in the drugs also have contributed to unnatural deaths although this is a minor problem compared with overdosing.

A report by the Advisory Council on the Misuse of Drugs ~ Reducing Drug Related Deaths indicated that heroin misuse is a major cause of drug-related deaths.

Some adverse effects associated with heroin abuse include septal necrosis, (the erosion and death of tissues between the nostrils, resulting from "snorting"), nausea and vomiting, loss of appetite and constipation. Slow and irregular heartbeat, an increased risk of strokes, heart attacks and blood clots also occur and exhaustion, increased vulnerability to accidents because of lapses in attention and concentration, and accidental overdoses because of uncertainty about purity levels. Chronic abuse has been associated with liver disease and respiratory complications such as pneumonia.

Even in the case of medically prescribed heroin in the UK during the 1960s, when addicts were maintained with 'clean' heroin there was a higher death rate compared with the normal population. Very often heroin abuse induces a form of lethargy and indifference to life, which in the case of some habitual users, leads to crime, an inability to work or irresponsible and anti-social behaviour.

A Report on a 33 year long study of heroin users by researchers at UCLA (May 14, 2001, Archives of General Psychiatry), has found that many users often suffer early death, hepatitis, HIV, sexually transmitted diseases and other health problems, and many have criminal justice histories. The study emphasises the pervasive public health and safety consequences of heroin abuse and the need for a comprehensive approach to deal with the problem.

Heroin has been used as a way of coming down from the energising effects of Ecstasy. An official Report published in France (23.7.01 The Guardian 24.7.01) indicates that it became popular with club-goers as a secondary drug to give them a "soft landing" from the highs produced by other substances. A new generation of users who would not consider injecting what has been regarded as a "dirty drug" in France, were content to snort lines of heroin in the same way that they would use cocaine.

The use of heroin during pregnancy poses the increased risk of complications such as miscarriage and premature delivery. Heroin is able readily to cross the placenta and so it is possible for the baby to become drug dependent. Consequently, the foetus may become addicted and suffer withdrawal symptoms requiring attention up to 8 days after birth. It is unusual for birth defects to result from heroin use although babies of heroin users are frequently smaller than average. Some studies have indicated developmental problems with the risk of low IQs and serious behavioural problems.

Heroin "Shooting Galleries": -

The proportion of the population, which uses heroin, in the UK, is relatively small, but the harm that is caused to both users and their immediate families, and the communities, is very serious. In 2001 it was estimated that there were approximately 250,000 problematic heroin users in the UK which is a huge increase on the estimate of just 1000, thirty years ago; that number was accepted by the Government in 2002.

The House of Commons Home Affairs Select Committee considered some evidence submitted about the treatment of heroin dependency by the prescription of diamorphine. It concluded that inadequate research and evaluation had been carried out and recommended further research as well as improved guidance and training to those practitioners licensed to prescribe diamorphine. The Home Office stated that a team of experts was considering the implications of a possible expansion of the prescription of heroin to addicts. In 2003 the Home Secretary indicated that he would approve the prescription of heroin to a relatively small number of people (around 400) and would provide training for licensed doctors.

(In 2005 Health Canada proposed the introduction of heroin prescriptions, particularly in Vancouver where the problem of abuse has reached epidemic proportions)

Despite the lack of research and evaluation the Select Committee was persuaded of the value of safe injecting houses or "shooting galleries" for addicts who would be able to continue their habit without fear of arrest in a safe environment where medical and practical advice would be available. The Committee recommended an evaluation pilot programme based on what it had heard about similar experiments elsewhere. The Home Office position was that such injecting rooms should not be introduced until proper evaluation becomes available of such trials in other European countries.

The Committee did not appear to take notice of the criticism of the Swiss Heroin Trials by a committee of medical experts under the auspices of the World Health Organisation. However, it did receive evidence from the Swedish Health Ministry to the effect that 'shooting galleries' are regarded in that country as effectively state-sponsored addiction. Nevertheless, the Committee recommended that the Government should commission a further trial to look at the prescription of diamorphine to long-term addicts who are not undergoing treatment.

In July 2006 the Elmfield substance misuse centre in Darlington was selected by the National addiction Centre, in London, to take part in a year long research trial where addicts can attend to inject only prescribed medication such as diamorphine and methadone. This trial will be partly funded by a grant from the National Lottery Fund and will be restricted to heroin addicts who have not responded to conventional treatment; thirty service users who have received treatment for at least six months (The Northern Echo 31.07.06).

Methadone.

Methadone is an 'opioid' – a wholly synthetic 'opiate like' product which was developed in Germany during the 2nd World War, when supplies of morphine became difficult to obtain. It is chemically unlike heroin but its effects are the same and it is, in itself, a highly addictive substance, which is used as a heroin replacement therapy, supposedly to wean users away from that drug. Its effects tend to be longer lasting such that one dose per day is usually sufficient. It is usually administered orally.

Tolerance and dependence may develop and withdrawal from methadone is more prolonged than from heroin although it is less severe. One of the original attractions about this drug was that its use was intended to reduce the illicit market for heroin, but this did not happen. Ironically this substance became as abused and addictive as heroin and there have been a high number of methadone related deaths. A black market for the substance developed before supervised treatment was introduced. However, drug users often take cocktails of methadone mixed with other dangerous drugs and there is evidence that many who receive methadone treatment also abuse heroin.

The Royal Pharmaceutical Society in the UK has expressed grave, concern about the rules regarding the dispensing of methadone because of the dangers to pharmacists from irrational patients. Pharmacy Inspectors recommended that only 10 methadone, patients per pharmacy is desirable, whereas in Edinburgh, which has the Scotland's largest methadone treatment programme the figures are often ten times the recommended number.

Between1992-96 the number of National Health Service prescriptions of methadone in Scotland more than doubled from 64000 to 164000. (Sunday Times 9.5.99)

The overall aim of substitute prescribing of methadone is intended to reduce harm by:

- Maintaining regular contact with the patient;

- Replacing street drugs of unknown purity;

- Encouraging a shift from a dangerous form of drug misuse, injecting, to a less dangerous one, oral;

- Controlling the dose of the drug with the aim of gradually reducing it,(although there has been much debate about how realistic this is).

The 30th Report of the World Health Organisation (WHO) Expert Committee on Drug Dependence in 1998, defined the main objectives of treatment for opiate dependence as being: -

- To reduce dependence on psychoactive substances

- To reduce morbidity and mortality caused by or associated with the use of psychoactive substances

- To ensure that users are able to maximise their physical, mental and social abilities and have access to services and opportunities to achieve full integration

- To reduce costs and risks to society

Additional objectives of treatment include a reduction in criminal and anti-social behaviour, a decrease in users' dependence on public (welfare) support, and an increase in productive, legitimate activities.

A survey undertaken in the cities of Liverpool and Manchester by "The Big Issue in the North" charity in 1999 revealed the following:

- of those on prescribed methadone, 80% also used street drugs on a weekly basis, particularly heroin. 44% on prescribed methadone used heroin on a daily basis.

- Although a quarter of users said they received counselling, many did not and twice as many said it was important as actually received it. Many patients believed they had been prescribed methadone by doctors who were ill-informed, about the drug problem.

- 17% of all those receiving prescribed methadone were injecting heroin and were not using needle exchanges.

- Virtually no respondents said that the drug services were aiming to provide a co-ordinated package of treatment including non-medical services to help them make progress in other areas of life. Most were unemployed.

- Many users had been attending services for a long time, most between 3-8 years and many felt that they were being maintained on an addictive drug as bad as heroin. Some users had been on methadone treatment for longer than12 years.

The Home Affairs Select Committee received evidence that methadone treatment is not universally available as a long-term intervention for all those who may need it in the UK. It became apparent during the hearings that there is widespread ignorance about the correct and appropriate dosages. For methadone maintenance programmes to be truly effective, it is thought necessary to back up the treatment with help in housing, employment, and general lifestyle problems. Methadone is not effective for all patients.

Research in the USA resulted in scientists announcing (May 2000 "USA Today" 31.5.00) that they were ready to launch alternative anti-addiction drugs for heroin addicts. The new drugs are considered less addictive than methadone. One such drug is called Soboxone and is a combination of buprenorphine and naloxone in a once-a-day pill. The significant difference about drugs containing buprenorphine and methadone, is that it is thought to be virtually impossible to overdose on heroin when buprenorphine is used

In January 2004 it was reported that the result of a small study by Johns Hopkins University School of Medicine in Baltimore indicated the distinct possibility that a single dose of long-lasting buprenorphine holds promise for the treatment of heroin addiction (Reuters Health 30.01.04). The lead author of the report stated that more research is needed to confirm the results and to identify the best use of the new formulation of buprenorphine. FDA approval for the drug is not likely to be forthcoming until more evidence is gathered.

Cocaine: -

Cocaine is the primary drug problem of the Americas but there are estimated to be 14 million abusers globally. The USA continues to be the largest cocaine market although a quarter of global users are found in Europe, especially in Spain and the United Kingdom but also in The Netherlands, Belgium, Ireland, Italy and Switzerland.

(UN World Drug Report 2005)

Cocaine is a central nervous system stimulant. It is a lipophilic alkaloid which is extremely potent and is a drug extracted from the leaves of the coca bush (Erythroxylon coca) which grows wild and is cultivated in the Andean Mountain region of South America; the largest producing countries are Colombia, Peru, and Bolivia. It is said to be one of the most dangerously addictive substances in the world and its derivative "crack" can be instantly so; it was used therapeutically and has some value as a local anaesthetic, but its production is now almost entirely for illicit purposes.

Until 1903, the popular drink "Coca Cola" contained a dose of cocaine. The Parke-Davis pharmaceutical company of Detroit was a leading cocaine manufacturer producing cigarettes, cordials, hypodermic capsules, ointments and sprays for 'over the counter' purchases. This contributed to large-scale addiction during the 19th century.

(The American Disease: The origins of Narcotics Control
– David F. Musto; New Haven: Yale University Press 1973)

The South American cocaine industry is said to cover a land area the size of continental USA. The profits of just one "drugs Lord" in 1998 were estimated to gross $200 million each week. The power associated with these profits enables the producers to corrupt and suborn many state officials and institutions and where financial inducement fails then ruthless people bring death and destruction to those who try to oppose them.

In its natural state, the coca plant thrives in the most adverse conditions and it has a life span of forty years. Several harvests of the leaves are possible each year and for many South American, peasant farmers the plant is the equivalent of "growing money on bushes".

In Peru, the Huallaga Valley is a massive area where extensive cultivation of the plant provides a living for millions of people who are either coerced or encouraged by powerful groups of Narco-terrorists. Cocaine is the country's largest export. There are no crops other than the coca bush, which can yield such large financial returns. However, the country claims to have achieved an almost two-thirds reduction of its 1995 crop. Bolivia has now become a marginal source for cocaine and overall these two countries now produce less than one fifth of the world cocaine (UN Global Illicit Drug Trends 2003). Nevertheless, both countries are encountering difficulties in consolidating this decline and eliminating the remaining illicit cultivation; resurgence in production is always a possibility.

The main challenge is Colombia where the production of cocaine from domestic cultivation has increased roughly by a factor of five in the years 1993-99. Since then the country has become the source of almost, three-quarters of the world's illicit cocaine although in 2002 it reported an impressive 37% decline in production since 2000. It has to be remembered that these figures are only approximations and Colombia is such a vast country that further development of the illicit trade is always a possibility. In the World Drug Report 2005 it was reported that production was increasing.

Some positive indicators are that the reported cocaine abuse in the USA has declined by 15% since 1998 and by 60% since 1985. There has been an increase in cocaine trafficking towards Western Europe where cocaine seizures have doubled in recent years

Production:-

Coca paste is extracted from the coca leaf and it takes approximately 100lbs of leaves to produce 1lb.of paste. The production of cocaine is a complicated and dangerous activity requiring a high degree of technical knowledge

The leaves are dried in the sun and then soaked in a mixture of alkali and water to produce a pulp, which is then washed in kerosene. When the mixture is drained, alkali is added and cocaine alkaloids are then produced which enables coca paste to be extracted; this in turn is dissolved in water, acid and potassium salt. The remaining liquid is separated and mixed with ammonia, which produces a form of pure cocaine. A further process, which produces cocaine as powder, requires this substance to be dissolved in dangerous chemicals and treated with hydrochloric acid; this crystallises the cocaine into cocaine hydrochloride and, when dried leaves a powder with 95% purity levels.

Early in 2004, it was reported that the Dutch Government had decided that it would refrain from prosecuting cocaine smugglers arrested at Schipol Airport with less than 3kg of the drug. The reason for this decision seems to be the large number of smugglers arriving at Schipol. This decision contravenes an EU Justice Ministers' Agreement of 27.11.03 to make the EU more efficient in the fight against drugs.

"Crack" cocaine is a crystalline and highly addictive form of the drug, which can be produced domestically in a microwave oven. Small amounts of "crack" in the form of white 'rocks' are sold at very low prices. 'Crack' has not yet become the epidemic drug in the UK that it is in the USA although there is great concern that the market is booming and with it the violent and armed conflicts between dealers, particularly West Indian "Yardie" gangs who sometimes distribute crack free to induce addiction and a larger client base (The Guardian 14.6.03). In September 2005 it was reported that there was estimated to be approximately 50,000 crack users in London and that the much feared epidemic appeared to be materialising. Another significant point arising from this research by the University of Bristol and Imperial College London was that many cocaine users were also reported to take heroin on a regular basis. (The Guardian 20.09.05)

Cocaine is used illicitly to create a feeling of euphoria, to overcome fatigue, and as a performance-enhancing drug. Its adverse side effects, besides dependency, are that it produces sleeplessness, chronic fatigue and it causes the heart to beat more rapidly and blood vessels to constrict; this in turn causes an increased risk of strokes and heart attacks. Heavy users complain of an itch often referred to as the 'cocaine bug'. Professor John Henry of St Mary's Hospital, London reported the results of a recent survey at the hospital that found that 7-10% of people arriving at A&E with chest pains had traces of cocaine in their urine. For the under 40s that figure rose by one third or as high as 50% on a Saturday night. In a control test of those without chest pain the figure was 3%. (The Guardian 24.09.05 and 24.10.05)

The American Heart Association published information in November 1999 of an increase risk of the development of aneurysms, particularly in younger abusers. High doses can induce toxic psychosis and paranoia. Depression and anxiety often follow as the effects of the drug diminish. Research at the University of Michigan (1999) indicated that cocaine use may produce long-lasting changes in the structure of nerve cells in certain areas of the brain, which is thought to contribute to addiction and the risk of relapse.

In confirmation of existing knowledge concerning heart attacks, the University of Harvard, Medical School research indicated that the risk of a heart attack occurring in the first hour after taking cocaine is 24 times greater than at other times (The Times 10.6.99). The British Medical Journal "Heart" published (May 2000) gives details of research undertaken at the University of Pittsburgh Medical Centre. This indicated that cocaine use results in the blood becoming more 'sticky', in the first two hours after use with the result that the risk of clotting is significantly enhanced.

The Report said – "The risk of thrombosis, similar to the risk of sudden cardiac death is real" (The Daily Telegraph 17.5.00). In the case of "crack", the effects are the same but for a lesser period of time, – sometimes lasting only 10 minutes - which is why addicts can spend so much money in trying to repeat the experience. The onset of "crack" induced euphoria is almost instantaneous and the intensity, although short-lived, is greater than that achieved with cocaine.

Cocaine abuse is becoming increasingly prevalent among women of childbearing age, and is associated with numerous adverse perinatal outcomes. The results of research, published in The Journal of Physiology (13.05.05), by Professor Lubo Zhang and his research team from Loma Linda University School of Medicine in California presented the new finding that cocaine exposure in utero has lasting adverse effects on the heart in adulthood, particularly in males.

Rarely, use of cocaine has resulted in birth defects of the brain, eyes, kidneys, and genital organs. Use during pregnancy has been associated with microcephaly in the infant as well as subtle cognitive and motor development abnormalities ("Special Issues" Gold MS et al 2005).The use of cocaine during pregnancy can also cause complications which may include premature delivery and premature detachment of the placenta (placental abruption) as well as low birth weight. Cocaine has been associated with the rise in foetal deaths in the USA where it is estimated that one in ten deaths results from the mother's use of cocaine during her pregnancy (The Guardian 24.10.05). The chances of miscarriage increase and newborn children may be hyperactive, interact less well and have learning difficulties which may continue to the age of five years or beyond.

("Special Issues" Gold MS et al 2005, Merck Manual
– 2nd Edition Drug Use During Pregnancy)

There is a greater danger of psychosis after extended use and "crack" cocaine is often associated with bursts of extreme violence. It is particularly dangerous for pregnant mothers to use "crack" because of the extreme likelihood of foetal damage, abortion, premature labour, small child size at birth and permanent development inhibition in infants. Cocaine mixed with alcohol is particularly dangerous, because this produces coca-ethylene which has a longer duration of activity in the brain and is more toxic than each of the individual drugs; it produces a much higher risk of death.

"Snorting" cocaine can result in septal necrosis (the erosion of the tissues between the nostrils); this is the most frequent method of ingestion, although injection is becoming more common since the advent of needle exchange programmes. "Crack" is usually smoked. It was reported late in 2004 (4) that a former neuro-surgeon consultant at the Royal Free Hospital in London, Dr Peter Harvey had found severe damage to the blood vessels in the brain after conducting Spec scans on regular cocaine users. In short, the scans have indicated 'holes' in the brain that could result in fatal brain seizures caused by restricted blood flow. Evidence of serious memory loss was found in some patients who were unaware of the damage they had suffered.

Withdrawal from cocaine is not as severe as for opiate addiction in that the body does not become physiologically dependent, but it does produce a state of unease, depression, and sleeplessness together with a psychological desire for the drug. There is some evidence of cocaine tolerance developing but this is thought to be short-lived; addicts have reported that they fail to achieve as much pleasure as they did from initial experience and they resort to increased doses. This has not been proved conclusively but the medical implications of cocaine abuse are enormous as it is a very toxic and life threatening substance.

Research in the USA by Xenova, a biotechnology company has developed a vaccine, which was on trial to assist those who have become addicted to cocaine. The vaccine produces antibodies, which attach themselves to the cocaine and prevent it from moving from the bloodstream to the brain – effectively eradicating any craving for the drug. In April 2002, an interim report was issued by the company indicating that it believed that good progress had been made with vaccine trials (The Guardian 5.4.02); the trials were reported to be successful in June 2003. Further trials were considered necessary before approval by the authorities would be possible and another report should be available in 2006. However, some experts doubt that a cocaine vaccine could ever be effective enough. "A line or two of cocaine contains approximately 200mg of drug which is a very large amount for the immune system to block".

(Professor John Henry, St Mary's Hospital London and
Imperial College of Science, Technology and Medicine)

There are thought to be over 100,000 people in the U.K .who use cocaine regularly. An upward trend in the use of cocaine has been noted since 1994, with the most dramatic increase being with 16-19 year olds, particularly young males.

Research, carried out by the National Institute on Drug Abuse in the USA, (NIDA June 1999), indicated that people dependent on cocaine come from poor backgrounds and have little support from family and friends. Those who suffer from depression or anxiety, require more intensive and lengthier treatment to assist them to overcome their abuse problems. Patients with moderate to severe problems are significantly more likely to achieve long-term abstinence if they receive at least 90 days of treatment. Drug treatment combining individual and group counselling, was found to reduce cocaine use more effectively than group drug counselling alone or supportive-expressive psychotherapy (The Archives of General Psychiatry – June 1999).

Research published in New York Academy of Sciences Annals (August 2001 by Professor Quinones-Jenab of NY City University) based on a ten-year study indicated gender susceptibility to cocaine use. Female users experience more excessive "highs" than do males, and this applies to alcohol and amphetamine type stimulants. Their use is affected by ovulation and this gives rise to a far more chaotic pattern of drug use than in men, leading to greater risks of dependency and overdoses. Female use is also affected by the contraceptive pill depending on whether it is oestrogen or progeston based. Most research has been based upon male models.

A new drug called Nocaine was under development and could help people overcome cocaine addiction; the drug was developed through Georgetown University Medical Center's Drug Unit in 2002 and it is thought that its effect would be similar to methadone in the treatment of heroin addiction.

In February 2006 it was reported that researchers at the University of California had identified a brain protein called 'orexin A' that appears to prompt craving for cocaine. This research could provide indications about the way to develop medications to block the craving.

("Neuron" February 16th 2006 – Borgland, S. et al.
'Orexin A in the VTA is Critical for the Induction of Synaptic Plasticity
and Behavioral Sensitization to Cocaine'. Neuron, 49(4), 589-601)

There was an agreement at the UN General Assembly Special Session on Drugs (UNGASS) New York 8-10 June 1998 to eliminate heroin and cocaine globally within ten years but this is widely regarded as an unrealistic aim.

Ecstasy, Amphetamine Type Stimulants (ATS), Depressants, Hallucinogens, Inhalants, Steroids, GHB, Rohypnol, Ketamine, Magic Mushrooms & Khat (Qat) and other 'designer drugs'.

ATS are synthetic drugs that include the chemically related amphetamine, methamphetamine and Ecstasy.

Unlike plant-based drugs, the production of ATS starts with readily available chemicals in small and easily concealed laboratories therefore production assessments are difficult but there are strong indicators that the expansion of the ATS is continuing at a rapid pace. In recent years trafficking in methamphetamine has expanded in East and SE Asia. In 2005 it was a major cause of concern in the USA with widespread abuse increasing significantly.

In 2000 close to 90% of all countries reporting to UNODC on methamphetamine trends indicated an increase; a year later this proportion had fallen to 52%. Thailand was badly affected because of massive exports from its neighbour Myanmar although Europe remains a major producer.

Ecstasy:-

Ecstasy is a designer drug hybrid, comprising a mixture of amphetamine and the hallucinogenic drug, mescaline. It comes usually in the form of tablets or capsules and it is almost always taken orally although it is sometimes "snorted" and rarely, injected.

Its full name is methylenedioxymethamphetamine (MDMA) and it has become widely accepted as a "recreational" drug by thousands of young people who use it both for its stimulant and hallucinogenic effects. Ecstasy if often referred to as the "dance drug" because it induces intense feelings of unlimited energy for people who attend "Raves" or night clubs, who speak about being able to 'dance all night'.

The drug increases visual and acoustic sensory perception and many users say that they lose all inhibitions and enjoy empathy and a sense of "togetherness" with the complete strangers who attend the event with them; emotional awareness is enhanced; for this reason it is also called the "hug drug".

In 1985 MDMA was grouped with Class A Drugs alongside heroin, cocaine and LSD and is classified as a dangerous drug. Its price varied from £7-£20 per tablet in the UK and up to $40 in the USA on the illegal market. However, research published in 2002 indicated that in some areas of the UK the price had fallen to as little as £1 per tablet and by the following year tablets in the UK sold for between 40-70p. It is believed that almost all of the available Ecstasy tablets supplied in Europe, originate in Holland (see Foreign Affairs May/June 1999 "Holland's Half-baked Drug Experiment"; see also Dazed and Confused - Smoke and Mirrors over Dutch Drug Policy Foreign Affairs Nov/Dec 1999). Large-scale production is known also to occur, in Belgium and Luxembourg. In the face of all evidence that is emerging to the contrary, that the Home Affairs Select Committee concluded that Ecstasy should be reclassified as a less harmful drug. The members seem to have arrived at that view based on the small number of deaths that occur and the opinion of one non-expert witness, rather than the overwhelming evidence that this drug does permanent damage to the structure of the brain.

The Committee pointed to the example of tolerance to drugs in Holland without mentioning the fact that the Dutch Government made provision of $16million p.a for 5 years, to establish 5 dedicated regional police, specialist Ecstasy/drug teams. Each team comprises 120 officers whose primary functions is to dismantle illicit laboratories, control precursor chemicals, increase EU co-operation to reduce the availability of Ecstasy, and to offer extensive public education about the harmfulness of this drug (INSCR 2002). Currently Holland is one of the major producers of Ecstasy. The Home Office rejected the proposal to reclassify Ecstasy.

More recently there has been evidence of massive production of these and similar tablets in SE Asia. One of the major international suppliers is Myanmar.

The drug has an exceptionally high profit margin – production costs running at a few pence per tablet and this has encouraged organised crime groups to become involved in marketing this highly dangerous but widely used drug.

It is too soon to be sure of all the possible side effects of Ecstasy, but there is sufficient known about the drug to demonstrate that it is a very dangerous substance, which has many adverse effects on users. It has been estimated that between 1-2% of the UK workforce is at risk from the use of Ecstasy.

(BBC News 11.7.01 – Dr Morgan, Researcher at University of Sussex)

Apart from the short-term feelings of euphoria and a general sense of wellbeing, there is increasing evidence that Ecstasy causes brain damage.

(see - Journal of Neuroscience 15.6.99 and study report in The Lancet, October 1998; also references in The Observer 7.7.96 and 15.12.96)

A study carried out by scientists at the University of Aachen in Germany, and published in the Journal of Neurology, Neurosurgery, and Psychiatry in May 2000, has indicated that even a light use of Ecstasy – as few as four tablets per month - can be harmful to the brain.

The study found that users performed worse in complex tests related to attention, memory, learning, and general intelligence tests than a group who did not use the drug. Furthermore, the study showed that performance deteriorated as consumption increased. The study was led by Dr Euphrosyne Gouzoulis-Mayfrank. A causal link with Parkinson's disease is possible (New England Journal of Medicine 6.5.99). Research emanating from the universities in London and Cambridge (June 2002) seemed to confirm this and further research by neurobiologists at St Jude's Children's Research Hospital, Memphis Tennessee in November 2005 reinforced these findings. Indeed the researchers also found from experiments with rats that a pregnant mother who takes cocaine may run the risk of passing the possibility of Parkinson's disease in later life to her unborn child. (The Guardian 14.12.05)

Any abuse of any hallucinogenic drug carries with it the risk of psychological problems such as confusion, memory loss, depression, excessive anxiety, and paranoia, all of which have been linked with the use of Ecstasy. Physical effects include nausea, muscle tension, blurred vision, faintness, sweating, chills, and other symptoms associated with heat stroke.

Malignant hypothermia occurs when the body loses the ability to control temperature and runs out of blood clotting agents. Death can occur from internal bleeding and organ failure. Problems have arisen because over-compensations for heat-stroke by excessive consumption of water, has led to death in several cases (hyponaetraemia – water poisoning).

Short-term problems include headaches, severe muscular pains, fatigue, and depression, which often appears several days after use (the "mid-week blues"). Longer-term use has been associated with psychosis and liver and heart damage; it has been suggested that MDMA may also suppress the immune system. A review of several studies by the National Institute on Drug Abuse in the USA (NIDA) has concluded that heavy MDMA users have significant impairments in visual and verbal memory compared with non-users.

(See The Journal of Neuroscience 15.6.99, and Psychopharmacology, April 1999)

Further findings by Johns Hopkins University and the National Institute of Mental Health (NIMH) suggests that MDMA use may lead to impairment in other cognitive functions, such as the ability to reason verbally or sustain attention.

Tolerance to the drug builds up quickly so that much higher doses are required to replicate initial feelings of energy and euphoria. There is too, an almost cavalier attitude to the number of tablets that are taken, amongst young people who simply do not fear or understand the risks involved; with increased consumption, there is a greater risk of damage.

Over 200 deaths in the UK have been associated with Ecstasy in the last few years but in many of the cases death has not been attributed to the drug's toxicity but rather to heat-stroke, excessive re-hydration (water overload) and heart failure. In 2001 researchers at the centre for addiction studies at St George's Hospital in London, reported that the number of deaths at 40 was double that of the previous year and four times greater than 1998. Most deaths have occurred because of heat stroke brought on by young people dancing to the point of exhaustion without the normal safety valve of feeling tired. Users have developed a great amount of body heat in less than desirable circumstances, often in very crowded and poorly ventilated dance halls, where sweating is ineffective in cooling them down. Collapse follows exhaustion caused by the excessively high body temperature, which results in reduced blood pressure and an increasingly rapid heart rate; blood clotting can occur which may result in death.

Resulting from the deaths in these circumstances, Local Authorities in many areas have attached conditions to entertainment licences, which require air conditioning, free and readily accessible drinking water, recovery rooms with first aid trained attendants. Additionally, notices about the dangers associated with drug taking which draw attention to the facilities available and recommending that dancers wear loose clothing are often displayed. The London Drug Policy Forum issued a code of practice on health and safety at dance venues, "Dance till dawn safely", and the Scottish Office has issued guidelines for Scotland. Despite these precautions, there is a possibility that their very existence may add to the misapprehension that taking Ecstasy is not a particularly dangerous activity. Central Government issued similar guidance in 2002 requiring all licensed clubs to make appropriate provisions.

Drinking too much water has the effect of diluting the necessary mineral salts in the body, whilst at the same time the drug has the effect of preventing the production of urine. The combined result is that the body becomes waterlogged and this induces chronic conditions leading to collapse and coma; kidney failure and swelling of the brain have been the result of excessive drinking in these circumstances and long-term damage to the liver and heart are likely.

Repeated high doses of Ecstasy can result in psychiatric illness and "flashback" experiences without further ingestion of the drug. Extremely high intake of Ecstasy can cause seizures and total collapse. Damage to the brain areas specifically associated with memory, perception, pain, sleep, appetite and sexual activity has been noted by American Researchers.

(The Lancet 10/98 – Research Report from The Johns Hopkins Institute)

Research into the abuse of MDMA continues but the widespread belief that it is a relatively "soft" and harmless recreational drug persists. The Swiss Supreme Court ruled (1999) that dealing in Ecstasy is not a serious offence. The Court acknowledged that Ecstasy "is in no way a harmless substance" and is illegal, but ruled that it cannot be said to pose a serious risk to physical and mental health, and does not usually lead to criminal behaviour.

The Supreme Court overturned a ruling from a court in Berne, which sentenced a man to one year in prison for selling 1000 tablets. At the same time, it rejected an appeal from a prosecutor in Aargau for a more severe sentence than the nine months imposed upon a dealer for selling 1300 tablets. Serious drug offences in Switzerland can carry sentences of up to 20 years in prison; no reason was reported for the Court's extraordinary conclusions.

(Associated Press in Lausanne reported in The Times 16.6.99)

The International Narcotics Control Board expressed concern about this ruling in its Annual Report for 1999. The Court held that MDMA is a "soft drug", the use of which "does not generally lead to criminal behaviour", and that it is mostly used by "socially integrated people". The INCB concluded that this was contrary to efforts by the international community to prevent the spread of trafficking and abuse of amphetamine-type stimulants (ATS).

Research published in The Lancet October 23 1999 (Vol. 354 pp1441-1442) indicated that Ecstasy might cause birth defects in addition to other known health hazards associated with the drug. Although it is not yet certain that there is a causal link between the drug and birth defects, the research findings are regarded as being sufficiently important, to warn young women who either are, or who are considering becoming pregnant, not to use the drug.

Research published by scientists at the Amsterdam Academic Medical Centre in October 2001 found that ecstasy causes injury to brain cells and long-term damage to memory. Study author Liesbeth Reneman said that users have fewer serotonin brain cells. This means that damaged brain cells can recover but fail to resume their function.

(Hassela Nordic Network 17.10.01)

Ecstasy is known to lower the brain's serotonin levels and this has been linked to depression, anxiety and the 'depersonalisation/de-realisation' syndrome in which sufferers feel completely isolated and cut off from the world.
Professor Una McCann of the US Institute for Mental Health compared 15 Ecstasy users with 15 who had never taken the substance. The Ecstasy users' brains were found to have significantly fewer crucial serotonin structures than those of the non-users (The Lancet 2001). Her conclusion suggests that people who use MDMA recreationally are putting themselves at serious risk of permanent, brain injury.

In January 2004 a report was published by a team comprising researchers from 5 universities led by Dr Jacqui Rodgers of Newcastle University, which indicated that regular users of ecstasy are risking damage to their long-term memory. Self-assessment by volunteers showed that those who use ecstasy are 23% more likely to suffer memory blanks than those who do not use them. Mixing ecstasy with cannabis, which is common, adds significantly to the damage. The research attracted responses from as far afield as the US, Australia and EU countries and the results conform to those achieved by actual memory tests. They are worrying and the researchers say that more study is needed.

In 2005 Dr Thomas Connor of Trinity College, Dublin stated that he believed from his research that Ecstasy is related to physical as well as mental illnesses. At a conference of the British Association for the Advancement of Science in Dublin he said: "Ecstasy has potent qualities which have the ability to increase an individual's susceptibility to disease," and he added that the environment in which these drugs are taken adds to that risk. Connor mentioned evidence that suggested that somebody taking two tablets would experience a weakening of the body's natural defences lasting up to 48 hours. However, research has yet to be completed on the long-term impact of Ecstasy on the immune system but Connor asserted the potential for damage in hard-core users.

(Reuters Health 7.9.05)

An additional problem that has been identified is the fact that MDMA is frequently replaced or partially replaced by other substances like MDA (Methylenedioxyamphetamine) or PMA (Paramethoxy-amphetamine). These compounds are designed as cheap "ecstasies" and are significantly more dangerous than MDMA. Even with testing kits it is difficult for users to know with certainty that what they believe to be Ecstasy is in fact MDMA, thus Ecstasy has an undeserved and dangerous reputation of safety among users. PMA is a club drug, which appeared at the end of the 1990s in both the USA and Europe. It exerts similar effects to Ecstasy, but has a less pronounced initial "high".

Some illicit laboratories produce PMA to resemble Ecstasy tablets. If the consumer thinks that he has taken Ecstasy and is disappointed with the effect, he may conclude that it has been diluted or "cut", and take more tablets to achieve the type of "high" that was expected from an Ecstasy tablet. This is very dangerous as the side effects of PMA include a rise in body temperature to dangerous ranges, which could be fatal. There is a failure of inner organs like heart, liver, kidney, and in 2000, 15 sudden death cases were attributed to PMA.

Research findings by Dr Lynn Taurah of the London Metropolitan University were presented to the British Psychological Society's Annual Conference (15.3.03 Bournemouth) at which she informed delegates that regular users of ecstasy took a distinct risk of falling into clinical depression. Her research looked at the habits of 221 young professionals and studied the difference between frequent and less frequent use of the drug also looked at former users, those who took cannabis and non-users. Her findings indicate that anyone using Ecstasy is at risk of depression but those who take large amounts have a significant chance of serious depression.

Dr Fabrio Schifano revealed his research that Ecstasy is very often taken as part of a cocktail of drugs he stated that those who take a large amount of drugs have an eight times greater risk of suffering depression than lower users. Out of the 202 ecstasy recorded deaths in England and Wales between 1997 and April 2002, 85% involved mixing ecstasy with other drugs. However, even small amounts of ecstasy pose a risk and there is no evidence yet of the long term effects of abusing the drug.

(The Observer 16.03.03)

In September 2003 the UN issued a report by Dr Schifano which indicated that the global production of Ecstasy exceeded 125 tonnes per annum and it estimates that 8 million people now take the drug on a regular basis - a 70% increase in 5 years. The combined market for ATS and Ecstasy is thought to be worth $65 billion per year and more people in Europe consume the drug than heroin and cocaine combined.

Amphetamine Type Stimulants (ATS)

Amphetamines are chemically manufactured drugs, which stimulate the central nervous system in a way that resembles adrenaline, one of the natural hormones in the body. They include dextro-amphetamine and methamphetamine. The drugs are usually dispensed in tablets, pills, or capsules and the most common method of ingestion is by swallowing although injection and inhalation are methods of abuse.

The chemical structure and the effects on the user are so similar that even regular users cannot tell the difference between them. Amphetamine was first dispensed in the 1930's as a readily available, 'over the counter' inhaler for nasal congestion and later it was prescribed for people who had difficulty in sleeping, and for what is now referred to as attention deficit disorder, and obesity. During WW II, the substance was used to prolong energy in the armed service personnel and it became widely available.

Abuse became very common amongst people, who needed to stay awake for long periods or who were on shift work, and athletes used it in attempts to achieve better performances. Amphetamines were also used to treat some mild forms of depression. By the 1960's, the potential for abuse was greater than most therapeutic uses and laws were introduced to restrict its availability; most doctors refrained from prescribing amphetamine although it is still legally available for this purpose.

The majority of amphetamines for abuse are produced in illegal laboratories and although their use is not as widespread as cocaine, methamphetamine used to be referred to as the "poor man's cocaine", before the price level of cocaine made it freely available and affordable. An increase in clandestine laboratories was reported during the 1990's and in the early 21st century methamphetamine use reportedly swept North America and became a severe social problem.

The effects of amphetamines are very similar to those of cocaine, although the onset is usually longer in occurring and the effects last for extended periods. There are many adverse effects associated with amphetamine; it is a highly addictive substance and a tolerance for it develops with frequent use. Regular abusers steadily increase their intake of the drug, sometimes reaching levels of consumption that may be many times more than the initial dose.

In the short term, the drug gives a feeling of wellbeing that lasts for up to 6 hours and assists concentration and endurance. However, amphetamines inhibit eating and sleeping and, in the longer term, produce exhaustion and intense feelings of hunger. A regular abuser becomes lethargic, heart rate increases together with blood pressure; the user may become dizzy, suffer from blurred vision, headaches, and sweating, and there is a danger of heart attack. These symptoms can be followed by loss of co-ordination, convulsions, and collapse. With excessive intake, the user may feel "driven" with mixed feelings of depression, unrest, and euphoria. High doses produce cycles of unproductive frenzied activity followed by exhaustion and extended sleep, which is then followed by further unrest and depression. Death has resulted from burst blood vessels in the brain, heart failure, and excessively high fever. Long-term effects include chronic sleeping problems, anxiety, poor appetite, high blood pressure and irregular heart rhythm, and skin rashes

Psychological addiction can occur and brain deterioration, hallucinations, and paranoia are a frequent result of prolonged abuse. Withdrawal from the drug can be difficult; confusion and memory loss for as long as a year has been reported. The abuse of methamphetamine has induced violence and, in cases where there is a predisposition to mental disorder, it has been reported that chronic psychosis has endured for several years. Some abusers turn to other addictive substances to help them cope with the undesirable effects of ATS.

Methamphetamine is not as common in the UK as it is in the USA where it is reported by ONDCP as one of the greatest drug threats in over 36 States with the majority use being predominantly in western States. Many clandestine laboratories are operated out of houses, hotel rooms and the boots of cars, but some "super labs" operate both within the USA and in adjoining countries.

In July 2005 researchers at the University of Toronto reported that a single prenatal dose of methamphetamine may be enough to cause long-term neuro-developmental problems in babies including reduced motor co-ordination. Meth abuse during pregnancy is known to be associated with low birth weight, cleft palates and other malformations but this research is the first indication of longer term mental damage. The developing foetus appears to be vulnerable to DNA damage from meth. exposure because it has not developed enzymes that would protect it from free radicals – highly activated, destructive oxygen molecules that have been implicated in cancer and neurodegenerative diseases.

("Free Radical Biology and Medicine" August 2005 – Professor Peter Wells.)

"Ice"

There is a variety of methamphetamine known as "Ice" (the street name for methamphetamine hydrochloride) which is in the form of clear or coloured (often blue, pink or green) crystals (Crystal Meth). These are smoked, inhaled ('chasing') snorted, injected or inserted anally, and produce an intense and enduring feeling of euphoria; it is highly addictive with a relapse rate of over 90% and has the same adverse effects as other amphetamines. However, "Ice" gives a very jittery high, along with anxiety, insomnia, and occasionally paranoia. An overdose can cause coma and death. Like Ecstasy, "Ice" appears to be neurotoxic to the brain and is a very dangerous substance; it is not yet widely known in the UK although concerns were reported in November 2005 that the drug was gaining popularity and thought to be manufactured illegally in domestic clandestine laboratories. It is relatively simple to make from easily obtained ingredients but because the chemicals are highly volatile home production can be particularly dangerous (The Guardian 15.11.05). It is associated with significant physical, emotional and social harms – more so than with other types of amphetamines. It can produce amphetamine psychosis which users of high doses may suffer with symptoms resembling paranoid schizophrenia. Withdrawal symptoms may include severe depression and a condition similar to Parkinson's disease, apathy, long periods of sleep, disorientation, energy loss, agitation, anxiety, a limited ability to experience pleasure and extreme exhaustion creating a desire /need to use more of the drug. It can also increase the heart rate and blood pressure resulting sometimes in irreversible damage to blood vessels in the brain and strokes. Long-term users suffer memory loss and the inability to think in abstract terms.

'Meth'

'Meth' addiction is difficult to treat because withdrawal often invokes insuperable depression and severe physical pain that has been described as being much worse than with heroin or cocaine, thus addicts often fail to complete recovery programmes and revert to the drug use.

'Meth' can be manufactured in domestic laboratories as basic ingredients are available in over-the-counter medicines and ordinary household products. Recipes are available on the internet and a basic chemistry set is adequate for production purposes.

Globally, methamphetamine and its variants, and amphetamine have together become more prevalent than heroin and cocaine combined and are much more widespread than Ecstasy. Major production occurs in Belgium and Holland but UK domestic production is reported to be increasing.

As a prescription drug it is still used in low doses for Attention Deficit Disorder and narcolepsy as well as obesity because it suppresses the appetite. However, there is concern about side effects and the availability of the drug for medical purposes has been restricted.

In June 2006 the Home Office announced that Crystal Meth would be included in the Class A list of dangerous drugs.

"Ya Ba"

This is a methamphetamine drug in pill form which is mainly produced in Myanmar (formerly Burma) from where millions of tablets are exported, mainly to Thailand. It is now becoming popular in the club/rave scene and appeared in noticeable quantities in the USA (2002). The Thai name Ya Ba (sometimes Ya-ba) is literally translated as 'crazy medicine', and an alternative name which has been coined is "Nazi Speed" because of its association with MDMA which was developed by the Germans during the Second World War. The drug is illegal and is said to be up to ten times more potent than Ecstasy, with a high that lasts for up to 10 hours. Ya Ba is an extremely addictive synthetic amphetamine substance which is highly addictive and extremely dangerous. Adverse effects include high blood pressure and body temperature, irregular heartbeats, which can induce strokes, and it has hallucinatory properties. In the longer term it can cause lung and kidney disorders. The drug is also associated with aggressive and violent behaviour.

The pills are small and are usually taken orally but sometimes users prefer smoke inhalation. Sometimes the pills are deliberately manufactured with logos similar to those, which appear on Ecstasy and they are manufactured with sweet flavours to make them more attractive to first time users. The pills are relatively inexpensive and their rapid spread has caused alarm in law enforcement and health agencies because of their potency and the possibility of almost instant addiction. Ya Ba has been described as the equivalent to amphetamines that 'crack' is to cocaine. One of the dangers is that there is no consistency of content or manufacture and so the chemical make up of the drug is unknown and may affect users in different ways.

Ritalin.

Ritalin (also known as methylphenidate): is a prescription drug used to treat hyperactivity in children. Since 1990, the use of the drug to treat attention deficit hyperactivity disorder (ADHD) has increased over 700% in the USA and its use is increasing in the UK. Unfortunately the abuse of this drug is also on the increase and according to information provided by the DEA school children are now popping, snorting, dissolving and injecting Ritalin in order to get high. According to the Christian Science Monitor (31.10.00) this is a popular drug in schools throughout the USA.

(See also The Times 8.11.00)

Research emanating from the University of Buffalo in November 2001 indicated that Ritalin may have the potential for causing long-lasting changes in brain cell structure and function. Ritalin is not a short acting drug.

(Joan Baizer, Professor of physiology and biophysics)

There have been reports that some abusers mix Ritalin with either heroin or cocaine to enhance the effects.

In February 2006 experts in the USA called for the drug to carry the highest-level warning that it may increase the risk of death from heart attack. 51 such deaths have been reported among children and adults taking the drug for ADHD since 1999. The Medicines and Healthcare Products Regulatory Agency (MHRA) said that 9 children had died in the UK.

(The Guardian 11.02.06)

Depressants.

These are legal drugs which are synthetically produced and which are often diverted for illicit use by abusers. They include benzodiazepines and barbiturates. Benzodiazepines are prescribed as tranquillisers and sleeping pills and include the more commonly known Valium, Librium, and Ativan each one of which has been associated with over-prescription and with what has been referred to as a generation of 'therapeutic addicts'. Many people in the UK have been treated for depression and associated problems with these drugs, and it has been estimated that one in seven adults are regular users of these and similar drugs, many of whom are addicted to them

Tranquillisers.

Tranquillisers are among the most commonly prescribed drugs. Abuse of benzodiazepines has adverse effects on the memory; and tolerance and dependence is common. It is difficult to withdraw from them because of psychological dependence. In the case of prescribed drugs, many people become addicted without realising this and use them as a permanent crutch to get them through life. Withdrawal effects include panic attacks, intense anxiety, and insomnia and a return to the depression for which they were prescribed. The abuse of these drugs is highly dangerous because the boundary between therapeutic use and potentially dangerous overdose is very narrow. Abuse carries with it a high risk of death from overdose and a combination with alcohol is particularly dangerous.

There is the distinct danger that people will take this prescribed substance and will drive a vehicle, or carry out other 'at risk' activities, without realising that they may be under the influence of drugs, or a combined effect of drugs and alcohol.

Barbiturates.

Barbiturates are a powerful central nervous system depressant, which can be prescribed, primarily for sedation or to induce sleep; because they are abused, prescription is not as common as it once was. Pills are swallowed and the effects of the drug last from 3-8 hours. Small doses act as a relaxant but larger amounts induce drowsiness, a lack of co-ordination and unpredictable emotional behaviour. Dependence and tolerance occur and the withdrawal experience is similar to that for benzodiazepines.

Hallucinogens.

An hallucinogenic effect can be obtained from both natural and synthetic drugs. Magic mushroom, contain psilocybin and some cactus plants contain mescaline, both of which are naturally occurring hallucinogens; mescaline is used in the synthetically produced Ecstasy.

Semi-synthetics such as lysergic acid diethylamide (LSD) and synthetics such as phencyclidine (PCP or 'Angel Dust') are the most commonly abused drugs of this type. It is not usual for hallucinogens to be used therapeutically, although some psychiatrists use them to induce a "mind-altered" state for the purposes of treatment and controlled experimentation.

Some trials were carried out with the military during the early 1960s in order to measure the 'psychedelic' effects (from the Greek psyche = mind and delos = visible); the results were so uncertain and sensual distortions were so great, that little medical benefit was identified. Even small doses of LSD cause major sensory distortions and those under the influence perform such dangerous and irrational acts that it has been classified as a highly dangerous drug: people have attempted to fly from high buildings or have performed equally dangerous activities. Physiological effects are slight but "flashbacks" without further intake of the drug have been reported months, and in some cases, years after initial ingestion.

There are three regularly occurring types of adverse reactions to hallucinogens: anxiety or panic attacks, depression, and psychotic disorders often resulting in flashbacks. These perceptual distortions have been called posthallucinogen perceptual disorder (PHPD). Strong emotions and events that bring about a recall of the circumstances when the drug was last used may trigger flashbacks. They may be induced by the use of marijuana or other drugs and in the case of LSD over a quarter of users will experience this phenomenon.

LSD is colourless, odourless, and tasteless and it is sold in tablet or capsule form, in gelatine squares or as transfers printed on small pieces of paper, usually with cartoon images on them. Users swallow the tablets and gelatine squares; they chew and swallow the paper, which has been impregnated with LSD liquid. Doses are now cheap and readily available and the effects last for anything between 2 and 12 hours, although the long-term after effects are uncertain and vary between users. "Bad trips" are frequently reported, in which users "freak-out" and experience horrific hallucinations which can result in extreme panic and paranoia, thus the consumption of hallucinogenic drugs is often a group activity in which experienced users assist one another through any unpleasant experiences.

Tolerance develops very rapidly and the experience of "good trips" usually outweighs the bad, although tolerance has a great potential for the longer term adverse effects such as "flashbacks" which can occur at any time and in any circumstances. Clearly, there is the distinct danger that these experiences might affect the users' work, driving ability, or their operation of complicated equipment or machinery. Physical dependence is not thought to occur with LSD.

PCP.

Phencyclidine is an anaesthetic, which was taken off the market when its adverse effects became known; patients experienced extreme agitation and some became totally disorientated, whilst others became violent, or aggressive. Other side effects include paranoia, delusions and suicidal thoughts. PCP is prepared as a white powder or in liquid form, both of which are very potent, and it is frequently added to marijuana "joints" to increase the "high" obtained from smoking them. Sometimes the liquid form of PCP is dropped onto ordinary cigarettes, or the powder may be sprinkled on food and eaten.

The effects last for several hours, but people have been known to take several days to recover. Sometimes users go on a binge, in which frequent doses are taken over the course of two, or three days, during which time the users neither eat nor sleep; this is followed by a period of physical exhaustion and deep sleep after which a deep depression is common. Physical dependence has been recorded and adverse effects include amnesia, paranoia, loss of weight, and increased heart rate, blood pressure and temperature, sometimes leading to coma or death by heart attack or respiratory arrest. Withdrawal symptoms include headaches, craving for the drug and "flashbacks" as in the case of LSD, which have been known to occur years later.

Inhalants.

Inhalants include a variety of industrial and domestic products, which are readily available, particularly to young people; they became a significant problem in the late1980's when a craze developed among schoolchildren who became convinced that the short-term effects were not dangerous. It was only when there were several highly publicised teenage deaths from the practise, that people became more aware of the dangers. Nevertheless, the use of inhalants is still widespread. It is common to see people in public places using paper or plastic bags with an inhalant inside, sniffing at the contents in order to enhance the feeling of intoxication; inhalation through the mouth is particularly dangerous and this practise is called "huffing". Destitute people who cannot afford drugs or alcohol will abuse common substances to achieve their "high"; although others, including young people still engage in this dangerous practice.

Inhaled substances include aerosols, glues, butane gas, lighter fuels, adhesives, cleaning fluids, nail varnish and paint. They produce an almost immediate "high" and a sense of euphoria induced by absorption of the fumes through the lungs. The sensation is similar to alcohol induced intoxication and the after effects can be much the same. Some of the inhaled substances depress the central nervous system and death has followed abuse very quickly because of respiratory failure. Oxygen deprivation to the lungs causes loss of consciousness, coma, and death.

Another, frequent cause of death has been when semiconscious users have suffocated from inhalation of their own vomit. Sudden interruption in the rate of heartbeat, induced by inhalation, can be dangerous particularly if strenuous activity takes place. The long-term effects of inhalation can be brain damage, amnesia, mood swings and, if nitrate based inhalants are used, increased pressure within the eyes leading to glaucoma and possible blindness. Where the solvents used are organically based, damage can occur to the liver and kidneys. The most apparent signs of abuse which parents should look for if they suspect that their children may be abusing inhalants are: -

- A distinct smell on their clothing;
- Inflammation around the nose and lips with rashes and nosebleeds;
- Loss of appetite;
- Loss of weight
- Listlessness and lack of motivation;
- Bloodshot eyes and dilated pupils
- The general symptoms of alcohol intoxication;
- Secretiveness and a lack of communication.

Inhalants are readily available and extremely dangerous with the distinct possibility that sudden death can occur even on the first occasion that solvents are misused.

Under the Intoxicating Substances Supply Act 1985 it is illegal to sell such items to people under 18 if it is thought that they will be abused. Similarly The Cigarette Lighter Refill Safety Regulations prohibit sale to anyone under the age of 18 years.

Gamma butyrolactone.

Gamma butyrolactone (GBL), an industrial solvent commonly used to clean graffiti, also has a darker purpose: the liquid can cause a euphoric high - or death - when ingested. GBL has become a popular intoxicant on the gay club scene, with sometimes deadly consequences. The drug can cause nausea and unconsciousness if too much is consumed. Users also risk damage to their stomachs, liver, and kidneys from ingesting the toxic solvent.

(BBC 7th October 2005)

There is evidence that some children exposed to inhalants pre-natally have suffered cognitive, speech and motor deficits.

("Special Issues" by Gold MS et al 2005)

Steroids.

There is ample evidence to show that the abuse of anabolic steroids is widespread. Usually the abuse is by athletes who seek competitive advantage but young and immature people have used them because they seek improved physical appearance. Steroids are usually swallowed as pills or capsules or injected intramuscularly. In the UK they are classified as a Class C drug. It is an offence to produce, supply, possess or import with intent to supply, but it is not an offence to possess them as a medical product, for personal use. Typical examples are Nadrolone, Testosterone, Sytanazolol and Tetrahydrogestrinone (THG) a so called designer steroid which is not produced by any pharmaceutical companies but rather by chemists seeking to deceive drug testing regimes.

With an appropriate diet and exercise, steroids can produce increased muscles, which help with strength, endurance, and rapid recovery time after strenuous activities. Nevertheless, they are classified as a harmful substance and most steroids are obtained illegally by diversion from medical or vetinerary sources. There is increasing evidence that the adverse side effects of these substances cause serious physical and mental damage. There are reports that the abuse of steroids can produce violent conduct in the user and complaints of domestic violence have been recorded where partners have taken steroids for the purposes of bodybuilding. Often these drugs are obtained illegally, at gymnasiums and health clubs.

In particular, there is specific evidence that steroids can produce liver, heart, and lung problems as well as damage to the reproductive organs. Steroids are directly related to testosterone and can cause abnormal breast development (gynaecomastia) in males and a reduction in the natural production of testosterone leading to infertility, baldness, severe acne, higher blood pressure, depressed sexual activity, and testicular atrophy. In females it can reduce breast size, interfere with the menstrual cycle, and produce masculine effects, such as increased body hair, and a deeper voice. Several of these effects are said to be irreversible. In adolescents, abuse of steroids can result in stunted growth.

Steroids are used medically in the treatment for inadequate levels of testosterone in humans; in the animal world, they are used to improve weight gain, coat appearance and to treat anaemia. There is increasing concern that the use of steroids in animals may adversely affect humans through the food chain and so the marketing of treated animals is controlled.

The abuse in sport is a problem which is inadequately countered by drug testing regimes, but athletes and their trainers have become so adept at managing the use of drugs that some abuses have become almost impossible to detect. Indeed, Hein

Verbruggen, President of the International Cycling Union is reported as saying that it is not possible to solve the problem of the misuse of drugs in the Tour de France annual cycle race (Sunday Telegraph 13.6.99). However, a combined urine and blood test for the banned blood booster erythropoietin (EPO) has been introduced for all major cycle races from 8th April 2001.

In July 2003 the UK government announced its intention to ban the use of four steroids in the androstene family, which are already prohibited by the International Olympic Committee, and are used by some athletes to build 'body bulk' and increase stamina.

GHB (Gamma Hydroxy Butyrate)

GHB is a central nervous system depressant that can relax or sedate the body. High doses can slow the breathing and heart rates to dangerous levels. It can be produced as a clear liquid, in tablet or capsule form or as white powder and is often combined with alcohol making it a potentially fatal substance. It is sometimes referred to as 'liquid Ecstasy' or "Grievous bodily harm" and is usually taken by young adults in the club scene. GHB is usually abused for its intoxicating effects but it can be used as a sedative and in this form, it has been used as a 'date rape' substance. It is also used for its hormone effects that can aid in muscle building.

The ingredients of GHB are gamma butyrolactone (GBL) and butanediol which are converted in the body into GHB. However, because of its illicit manufacture, the concentration of the drug can vary significantly and this creates an added danger to its abuse. Its effects occur within 10-20 minutes from ingestion and last for approximately 4 hours. Overdose can occur very quickly and may result in coma or death; the signs of this are similar to other sedatives – drowsiness, nausea, vomiting, headache, loss of consciousness, loss of reflexes, and impaired breathing. GHB clears the body very quickly and is sometimes difficult to detect in hospital emergency rooms. Consumers are often left with no recollection of events whilst under the influence of GHB, hence its attraction as a 'date-rape' drug.

In August 2003 the UK government announced that this substance would be illegal making possession of the drug without a medical prescription punishable by up to two years imprisonment; supplying the drug illegally attracts a sentence up to 5 years. The drug was placed in category C under the Misuse of Drugs Act 1971.

Ketamine.

Ketamine is an anaesthetic administered to both animals and humans by injection, although 90% is for animal use. It gained popularity as a club drug in the US in the 1980s when it was realised that large doses caused a similar reaction to that of PCP, such as hallucinations and dream-like states. It is produced in liquid form or as a white powder, which is 'snorted' or smoked with marijuana or tobacco products and it is often consumed with other drugs.

High doses can cause delirium, amnesia, impaired motor function, high blood pressure, depression, delirium and agitation, and potentially fatal respiratory problems. Low dose intoxication results in impaired concentration, poor learning ability, and memory loss. From 1st January 2006 it became classified as a Class C drug and is therefore illegal.

Rohypnol ® (flunitrazepam)

Rohypnol belongs to a class of drugs known as benzodiazepines such as Valium and it is not approved for prescription use in the USA although it is in Europe where it is used in the treatment of insomnia, as a sedative and in pre-surgery anaesthetic. Rohypnol is tasteless, odourless and dissolves easily in carbonated drinks; its sedative and toxic effects are aggravated by alcohol. Even without alcohol, it can impair a person for between 8-12 hours. Although the substance is normally taken orally there have been reports that it has been ground up and 'snorted'.

Those who consume Rohypnol seldom remember events experienced while under its influence, hence its popularity as a 'date rape' drug. Other effects of the drug include decreased blood pressure, drowsiness, visual disturbance, dizziness, gastrointestinal upset, and water retention.

Cigarettes soaked in embalming fluid have been reported as a type of date-rape drug (The Guardian 14.10.05). The cigarettes, referred to as "fry" cigarettes, are tobacco or cannabis cigarettes dipped in embalming fluid. The fluid comprises formaldehyde, methanol, ethyl alcohol or ethanol, and other solvents. Sometimes, the compound used in the "fry" cigarettes is phencyclidine (PCP). This drug adds a high level of danger and may be lethal. According to a 1998 study by the Texas Commission on Alcohol and Drug Abuse, those who smoke "fry" cigarettes experienced toxic psychosis, hallucinations, delusions, and sometimes, unconsciousness.

Khat (qat)[pronounced cot]

Khat is a flowering shrub native to NE Africa and the Arabian Peninsula. The leaves are shiny and crimson/brown in colour and appear similar to Basil. The plant is legal in the UK but is banned in Europe, and North America. In 2004 it was reported that the UK Government was considering the possibility of banning it and in 2005 it was referred by the Home Secretary to the Advisory Council on the Misuse of Drugs for a recommendation. The Khat plant itself is not controlled under the Misuse of Drugs Act, but the active ingredients, cathinone and cathine, are Class C drugs. Cathininone may not be lawfully possessed or supplied except under a licence for research, though cathine may be prescribed. The legal status of khat is currently under review. It is controlled by law in countries such as an America, Canada, Norway and Sweden.

It is usually chewed and users claim that it is a stimulant, which gives them energy, and sharpens their thought processes. Effects are similar to those induced by cocaine and amphetamine, but are less intense.

If taken in excess it causes extreme thirst, hyperactivity, verbosity, a loss of appetite and wakefulness. Repeated and continuous use can cause manic behaviour, paranoia, and hallucinations. It can also damage the respiratory, central nervous, circulatory and digestive systems and it has been linked with mouth cancer. Chewing Khat during pregnancy has been associated with low birth weight in newborn babies. The active ingredient in Khat is cathinone, which is classified as the equivalent of a Class A drug in the USA. Cathinone is an unstable chemical and within 48 hours of the plant being harvested it breaks down to the less potent cathine. There is another class of chemicals in khat known as cathedulins which also make the brain release dopamine, the feel good neurotransmitter chemical but it is not known (2004) what effect they may have on the brain in the long-term.

(The Guardian 5.2.04)

Magic Mushrooms.

Psilocybe mushrooms were classified as a Class A drug in July 2005 (section 21 Drugs Act 2005) – the only exceptions are for wild mushrooms growing on uncultivated land. Landowners who are unaware that they have a controlled substance, or who pick them with the intention of delivering them to police will be exempt from prosecution. From 18th July 2005 importation, possession or sale of magic mushrooms became punishable with life imprisonment. There is evidence that the use of such mushrooms could trigger psychosis.

Other 'designer drugs'

With the development of the Internet it has been possible for some people to purchase 'designer drugs' online. These psychedelic drugs that are known euphemistically as "research chemicals" have been available mainly from websites in the USA. In 2004 the Drug Enforcement Administration closed down some sites and made arrests after at least two deaths and several cases of people requiring hospital treatment after consuming chemicals purchased in this way. Customer records and credit card details indicated a British connection and in 2005 several arrests were made in the UK and a variety of drugs were seized including one known only as 2C-I popular in clubs and sometimes called the "new ecstasy".

The chemicals have effects similar to those caused by mescaline, ecstasy (MDMA) and LSD and most have not yet acquired street names but are known only by abbreviated laboratory codes such as 5-Meo-DMT, 2-CT-2 and AMT (alpha-methyltriptamine). Many of these chemicals are too powerful in their effects to be popular but they are potentially very dangerous. When smoked 2mg of the chemical 5-Meo-DMT can produce a short but very potent "trip" and heavy doses can cause serious side effects including overheating of the body and in some cases – death. These chemicals have been produced by underground chemists seeking to outpace international anti-drug laws however The Misuse of Drugs Act was amended in 2002 to include a clause that effectively outlaws all chemicals used for illicit purposes.

(The Guardian 25.05.05)

The Abuse of Prescription Medicines.

Many prescription medicines are either stolen or obtained fraudulently and misused for illegal purposes and this includes methadone, Ritalin and cough medicines. In the USA drug abusers have been abusing a slow release pain killer in the form of fentanyl patches to enable them to get a dangerous 'high'. This trend has resulted in a significant number of fatalities and researchers at the University of Florida drew attention to this particular problem in July 2005. 115 abusers died in Florida in 2004 but the abuse is a nationwide problem.

Addicts are reportedly using a clear patch that is designed to transfer a controlled dose of fentanyl through the skin into the bloodstream over the course of a few days. The patch is typically prescribed to treat postoperative or chronic pain conditions but abusers are extracting the whole dose and using in circumstances that amount to a dangerous overdose. Fentanyl was first synthesised in Belgium in the late 1950s and has an analgesic potency about 80 times that of morphine; it is used extensively to treat cancer patients.

CHAPTER 7
Drugs in the Workplace.

Why should employers be concerned about the impact of drugs and alcohol in the workplace?

For those who are fortunate enough to be in full-time employment, nearly one third of their lives will be spent in the workplace and there is ample evidence available that demonstrates that it is not possible to separate health and social problems from work. Although little research outside the USA has been conducted about the problems associated with drugs in the working environment, evidence gained from studies on alcohol together with the world wide growth in the abuse of drugs gives rise to serious concerns about the adverse impact of drugs on businesses.

Studies carried out in the USA indicate that 73% of regular drug users are in employment. In the UK, such information as is currently available indicates that at least 24% of regular drug users are in employment but that figure is certainly much higher. Studies in the European Community carried out by the International Labour Office (ILO) in 1993 indicated that there was a growing concern about this issue and the extent to which drugs and alcohol were affecting hundreds of thousands of workers.

(UN World Drug Report 1997 pp101-02)

It is important to remember that comparisons of statistics are not always reliable. The USA includes alcohol as a drug, whereas others make a distinction between drugs, alcohol, and legitimate medications. Nevertheless, the concerns are common and the adverse effects of alcohol and both licit and illicit drugs on businesses can be profound and very costly. Although a worker may not carry out his habit during working hours the effects of private use elsewhere can have devastating effects in the working environment and employers should be alert to avoid the consequences of this growing problem.

The misuse of drugs and alcohol can impair efficiency, increase absenteeism and job-related accidents, increase production costs and seriously affect the safety both of the worker, his colleagues, and the end user of the product. The Home Office estimated that there were over 200,000 addicted drug users in the UK, many of whom are in employment (Drugs-The Business Agenda 1999). This estimate was revised to 250,000 in evidence to the Home Affairs Select Committee in 2001. Additionally, there are many thousands of casual drug users and hundreds of thousands of people who can be classified as having an alcohol related problem, who are in employment.

According to "Business in the Community", in the publication 'Drugs – The Business Agenda', as a basis for success business needs:-

- A stable environment which is attractive to investors
- A skilled, flexible and motivated workforce and
- A prosperous consumer base.

Drugs and alcohol undermine all of these factors. They are psychoactive substances, the effects of which remain with the user for a considerable time after use, and which are permanently present and affecting the mind and body in those who are regular or addictive users.

These substances impair working efficiency. This results in - loss of concentration, poor judgement, low quality performance, increased absence, more accidents, increased health care costs, high staff turnover rates, additional costs of recruiting and training new staff, loss of revenue, damage to reputation, increased warranty costs and an increased risk of legal liability for damages. There is too the increased likelihood of crime, with a corresponding impact on the business either by actual losses from theft, fraud, or criminal damage within the business or from deterioration in the social and economic conditions that allow a business to prosper.

It has been estimated that up to £10 billion per annum is lost to legitimate business in the UK by drug users spending a significant part of their disposable income on drugs rather than on legitimate commercial products and services. The tax burden on business is increased by additional costs falling on the Social, Health, Criminal Justice, and Education systems.

Additional damage is caused when stockholders lose confidence in the efficiency of a business blighted by drugs and alcohol and move their investments elsewhere. All of these factors affect both the efficiency and the profitability of a company and yet it is believed that fewer than 20% of UK companies have comprehensive substance misuse policies in place.

In 1983, only 3% of the largest companies in the USA were employing substance misuse policies which included testing for drugs and alcohol. By the early 1990's, the impact of drugs had become so widespread, and the concerns had become so great, that this percentage had increased to 98%.

Within a period of seven years the recognition that drugs could seriously jeopardise a company's ability to stay in business brought about a profound change in attitudes amongst business people who had, hitherto, ignored the potential for harm. It was only when these employers witnessed well educated, highly trained and experienced employees losing their careers, their families and their futures to substance abuse, as well as damaging the companies for whom they worked, that they took action.

The most extensive studies of drug and alcohol use in the workplace have been carried out in the USA and the results of some of those studies are worth considering:

- According to the Department of Health and Human Services' 1996 National Household Survey released in 1997, over 70% of all adult illicit drug users were employed and in an average month –
- 32 million Americans engaged in binge drinking
- 13 million used illicit drugs
- 10.1 million used marijuana
- 1.7 million used cocaine
- 11 million had 5 or more drinks per occasion, 5 or more times per month.

According to the Department of Labor, the annual cost of on-the-job substance abuse is estimated to be one hundred billion dollars ($100,000,000,000). This figure includes lost productivity, theft, accidents, and additional health care costs.

Studies reported by the Institute for a Drug Free Workplace show:

- of all workplace drug users who test positive, 52% are daily users;
- Employees who test positive for drugs were 60% more likely to be responsible for plant accidents, use a third more sick leave, and have more excused absences;
- One national automobile manufacturer reported that drug-using employees averaged 40 days sick leave p.a. compared with 4.5 for non-users;
- The estimates are that expenses and losses related to substance abuse average 25% of salary for each worker affected.

The U.S. Postal Service conducted a 3-year study ending in 1990, which provided incontrovertible evidence that drug-using employees performed less well compared with non-users. The Service hired people regardless of the pre-employment screening results but monitored their progress over the course of three years. Those employees who tested positive for marijuana had 55% more work related accidents; 85% more injuries; a 78% higher rate of absenteeism and they committed 55% more discipline offences than those who had tested negative. In the case of those showing positive for cocaine use, the absentee rate was 145% higher than non-users and the injury rate was 85% higher.

(Normand.J., Salyards.S. 'An Empirical Evaluation of Pre-employment
Drug Testing in the US Postal Service).

The Georgia Power Company examined the relationship between illicit drug use and workplace performance by comparing records between users and non-users. Drug users were found to have consumed almost twice the medical benefits of the non-using-control group; were absent 15 times more often and made twice as many workers' compensation claims.

(Osborn & Sokolov 'Drug Use Trends
in a Nuclear Power Company' UN World Drug Report 1997).

Employers, who have instituted drugs testing for employees, believe that it causes the rate of employee drug use to fall. Statistics published by Smith, Kline & Beecham Clinical Laboratories in Collegeville, Pa. indicated a drop of positive tests from 18.1% in 1987 to 5% in 1998. In May 2000 a study conducted by the Cornell School of Industrial and Labor Relations in relation to the construction industry indicated that where construction companies had adopted testing practices there was on average a 51% reduction in injury rates within 2 years of adopting testing programmes. Companies who adopted testing found that they saved substantially on workers' compensation premiums when compared with companies who had not adopted testing. 72% of the companies with drug testing in place said they believed the benefits of drug testing outweighed the costs and that their programmes had a positive impact in virtually every respect.

("An Evaluation of Drug Testing in the Workplace:
A Study of the Construction Industry," Jonathan Gerber).

In 1982 the US Navy began random drug testing after an aircraft accident on its carrier USS Nimitz; the most common drug of abuse was found to be marijuana and between 1982 and 1987 the overall positivity rate dropped from 48% to just 3% after testing was introduced. The practice spread to other branches of the military and was then introduced into safety sensitive government agencies such as the Nuclear Regulatory Commission. The Drug-Free Workplace Act, 1988 required many federal grantees and contractors to provide drug-free workplaces. Several fatal accidents in the transportation industry, where drivers had tested positive after the event, resulted in the passing of the Omnibus Transportation Employee Testing Act of 1991.

The impetus for the introduction of substance abuse policies in the workplace, including testing, spread from the large corporations to small and medium sized businesses. There was a realisation in the USA, that drugs and alcohol have been hugely damaging to business and that employers must share the responsibility for doing something about the problem. That realisation is only just beginning to occur in the UK and Britain has lagged behind the very positive example given by the United States. In 1999 the UK's Anti Drug Co-ordinator recognised and advocated the need for appropriate substance misuse policies, including testing, in the workplace. Unfortunately this advice had been available, but largely ignored for over a decade, by a complacent industry that did not believe that the drug epidemic would affect the UK.

In the UK a compulsory drug testing programme was introduced for the armed forces in 1998. Since then positive test rates have fallen to 0•9% compared with an average of 5% in civilian workplaces. The services have adopted a zero tolerance policy leading to the dismissal of those who test positive or admit to using drugs.

(The Guardian 26.09.05)

Obligations upon an Employer/business person.

The law of tort in the UK places a general duty of care upon employers/business people to take all reasonable precautions to ensure that nothing done by them causes damage to their neighbours. More precisely, there is also a general duty under the Health & Safety at Work etc. Act 1974 for employers to ensure, as far as is reasonably practicable, the health, safety, and welfare at work of employees. Appropriate Regulations require employers to assess the risks to health and safety of employees in their working environment (Management of Health and Safety at Work Regulations 1999). Thus, an employer who knowingly permits an employee to be at work under the influence of drink or drugs, to the danger of that or any other employee, commits a criminal offence.

Employees are required to take reasonable care of themselves and others who could be affected by what they do in the course of their employment. Various other statutes make it a criminal offence for certain workers to be unfit through drink or drugs while working on railways, tramways, or other guided transport systems. The Misuse of Drugs Act, 1971 is the principal UK legislation controlling the misuse of drugs and anyone who knowingly permits the production or supply of drugs, the smoking of cannabis or certain other drug-related activities on their premises commits a criminal offence. This applies not only to employees but also to contractors, sub-contractors, customers, and visitors who may use the premises.

Thus, the employer who connives at the misuse of drugs on his premises rather than implementing substance misuse policies and taking reasonable precautions against misuse may be committing an offence in addition to risking his business. The Road Traffic Act, 1988 creates offences for any person driving, attempting to drive or being in charge of, a vehicle whilst unfit through drink or drugs. Employers who allow employees to act contrary to the law may be guilty of aiding and abetting the offences.

Substance Misuse Policies for the Workplace.

In view of the publicity that has been given to the drug problem in the UK, it is no longer reasonable for employers to fail to consider the need for an appropriate substance abuse policy, which may include testing for drugs and alcohol. This issue does not now attract the opprobrium that once it did, and the heated arguments that had turned on such vague terms as "invasion of privacy, civil rights and big brother tactics" are no longer common. Nevertheless, we are far from a universal acceptance of the need for such policies; the UK has a long way to go before it emulates the standards that are commonplace in many working environments in the United States.

There can be little doubt that all organisations would benefit from adopting an agreed policy that has been fully discussed and explained to all members of staff. Such policies must apply at all levels of the organisation from boardroom to the shop floor, as drug misuse has no social or cultural boundaries.

Apart from protecting the business interests of the company by developing policies and procedures employers can set a good example and have a significant impact on bringing about demand reduction in the general campaign against drugs. It is likely that the most successful projects will be those that take place in an environment where common values and practices are shared in a joint community initiative involving other local businesses, the local authorities and members of the community. "Business in the Community" has identified what it sees as the benefits of business involvement in such initiatives where opportunities can be created for: -

- A more cohesive and prosperous local community

- A stable, committed workforce

- Improved staff performance

- Reduced local crime

- Lower costs for items such as insurance and security

- Cost effective employee training and development

- Team building activities

- Improved employee morale and company pride

- Enhanced recognition, market position and branding

- Positive media coverage

- Higher standing in the community

- An improved corporate image with investors.

As part of its effort to encourage employers to adopt substance misuse policies the US Drugs Enforcement Administration (DEA) published Guidelines for a Drug-Free Workforce 2nd Edition April 1998. This document draws heavily on the expertise of many organisations and Government departments in the USA, with particular reference to the Houston Drug Free Business Initiative.

(Calvina Fay - now CEO of the Drug Free America Foundation)

The guidance is similar to that which has been published elsewhere and, is a comprehensive document, which describes the steps that a concerned employer should follow when considering what to do about the issue of drugs. In the UK the Health & Safety Executive (HSE) has published a guide for employers entitled 'Drugs Misuse at Work' which offers advice along similar lines to that provided by the DEA but in less detail.

Summary of Recommendations for a Drug-Free Workforce.

In order to achieve a drug and alcohol free workforce, employers must take a comprehensive approach, which should include:-

A Written Policy – this document should be a clear statement of the company's aims objectives and responsibilities. This should be agreed with the workforce and acknowledged in writing by each employee who accepts personal responsibility by agreeing to the policy. The document should include a statement on the company's position on drugs and alcohol; the company's intentions in the case of a breach of the policy; the company's expectations of the employees; a statement regarding any sanctions, treatment programmes, counselling, etc. Terminology should be clear and unambiguous with appropriate definitions where necessary. For example, drug abuse may be defined as - " any activity involving illegal drugs, chronic or improper use of alcohol, and misuse of over-the-counter and prescription medicines. It could include failure to notify the employer that an employee is taking medication which might affect his/her ability to carry out the assigned tasks safely and competently".

A commitment to confidentiality should be included. If testing is to be part of the policy, a separate document should describe how that procedure will be carried out. A policy statement should not be confused with procedural details, which should be covered in separate documents.

The policy should change only rarely although it should be subject to annual review and it should be monitored for effectiveness and cost. Policies and procedures should be kept under constant review and will probably change periodically. It is a good practice to have a policy even if there is no evidence of a problem within the organisation. Establishing a policy will enable an employer to demonstrate that he has fulfilled his legal obligations and will assist in dealing with any problems that may arise.

Potential Problems/Risk Assessments. It is essential that an employer should make a careful examination of records not only to discover if there is a problem but also to enable an assessment of the effectiveness of any policy. This review should include – sickness, productivity, accidents, discipline, and morale. Employers should consult with Managers and Supervisors, Safety Representatives, Union Officials and employees either in the course of special meetings, appraisal reports or by inviting suggestions, ideas, or comments. It is sensible to obtain information and advice from other employers who have already adopted a policy; from business and trade associations and from the local or national Health Authorities and specialist drug and alcohol agencies. Obtain specialist advice and involve the employees.

Education and Training Programmes. It is sensible to provide information and training sessions to advise all employees of the company's policies and the likely health and legal consequences of failure to follow the policy.

Any good organisation will provide continuing education particularly insofar as it affects safety. A healthy and safety conscious workforce will be more productive. Most people, including management, are not well informed on the subject of substance misuse and most will not have considered the consequences of the effects of drugs and alcohol misuse. There should be regular meetings, staff discussions, notices/posters, payslip "flyers", and even an introductory booklet or induction course for all employees on joining the company, which emphasise the importance of, and reasons for the policies. It is wise to ask employees to sign that they have read and understood relevant information. Records should be kept, particularly of attendance at training sessions. Liaison with other companies will reinforce the value of such policies.

Information should always be current and should not lose its impact by neglect. It is valuable to publish widely the signs and symptoms of drug and alcohol impairment. It is important to create a safety culture and to proscribe unnecessary drugs and alcohol from the workplace. Special attention must be given to those on medication who must be encouraged to declare their current use, particularly if it is 'safety sensitive', and staff should not be financially penalised – e.g. by being put into a less well paid job while on medication.

Employee Assistance Programmes. An employer should consider what approach is to be taken in cases of breaches of policy. Blatant disregard of the law can be treated as warranting instant dismissal but employees who have a drug or alcohol problem are entitled to the same rights as if they had any other recognised medical condition.

As far as possible, drug and alcohol misuse should be treated as a health issue rather than a case where immediate disciplinary sanctions are invoked. Where no law has been broken, it is likely that an Industrial Tribunal in the UK will judge that an employee has been unfairly dismissed if an employer has made no attempt to help a person with a medical problem.

Where safety is involved, it may be appropriate to move an employee with such a problem to another job, which is not safety sensitive. Confidentiality is essential. If rehabilitation is offered, it is necessary to decide whether this is a once only option and whether the company or the employee will assume the costs involved. It may be more beneficial to rehabilitate a highly trained employee, than to dismiss him and recruit and train a replacement. The policy must operate fairly for all employees. It is a good idea to maintain a list of treatment facilities to which employees may turn for help.

Management and Supervision training. If the people who are most likely to identify any problem are not kept up-to-date with information on how to identify the signs and symptoms of drug and alcohol misuse, then the policy is likely to be less effective. If the organisation is large then the company doctor and nurses can give regular advice and guidance; if the company is small then it may be necessary to bring in professional help.

Drug and Alcohol Testing. Employers should consider implementing a drug and alcohol testing policy to detect and deter abuse, and as part of the occupational health policy. The purpose of testing is to ensure a drug and alcohol free workplace. Screening is normally conducted in the following circumstances: -

- Pre-employment testing as part of the selection process;
- Routine, unannounced and random testing as part of an agreed policy;
- With cause, after an accident or unusual incident, or as part of a rehabilitation process.

If such a programme is adopted it should be made a condition of employment to which all employees sign their agreement. It is essential that such programmes are impeccably fair and reasonable and that an appeals process is included. Most employers contract this work with a reputable and independent organisation, which should guarantee the following:-

- The laboratory should provide guidance on collection procedures to ensure continuity of evidence, correct storage, and prevention from contamination, deterioration, and tampering with specimens.

- The supply of a procedurally correct and up-to-date manual of laboratory practices and procedures.

- Testing by trained and experienced technicians.

- The supply of appropriate containers without preservatives and preferably with a temperature strip. If necessary the contractor should supply all report forms, evidence tape and tamper proof labels and should provide an evidentially correct courier service. Confidentiality should be guaranteed.

- The laboratory must assure that all positive tests are submitted for confirmation by gas chromotography/mass spectometry (GC/MS) procedures.

- Testing should be specific and should distinguish between illegal substances and legitimate medications. Refrigerated storage of positive samples must be available. Results must be confirmed in writing and an employer should never act on a verbal report alone.

- Expert testimony should be available where evidence by certificate is not acceptable.

- Laboratory personnel themselves should be subject to drug/alcohol testing programmes.

Job Descriptions and Employee responsibilities; the company should identify and publish the expectations that it has of its employees, e.g. :-

- Employees should report for work unimpaired by the use of alcohol, drugs, or medicines.

- Alcohol should not be brought to or consumed on the premises except in clearly defined and exceptional circumstances.

- Any employee who is using prescribed or purchased medicines, which may impair work performance, should notify a supervisor before commencing work.

- Employees must not use drugs proscribed by law at any time.

- All employees must exercise a duty of care to their co-workers and where they have cause to believe that the performance of another worker is impaired by reason of alcohol, drugs or medicines or for any other reason, they must report their concerns to a supervisor.

Signs and symptoms of Impairment through drugs or alcohol.

It is important that supervisors should be aware of the indicators that may identify a problem in the workplace, but it is also a good practice to give employees some basic information. Training enables supervisors to establish reasonable suspicion before referring employees for testing and helps in maintaining welfare of employees who may have problems that are not related to substance misuse. It is important that all training is fully documented and, in the case of supervisors, is noted on personal records.

Drug and alcohol abusers can be identified by observation, by performance review and by noting the associated paraphernalia of their habit e.g. alcohol containers, specific drugs and using equipment. In the case of drugs it is a wise precaution to bring in expert assistance such as a police officer, who will be able to demonstrate the types of equipment associated with drug use, associated with alcohol – the smell of alcohol, glazed eyes, dilated pupils, slurred speech, an unsteady gait and lack of co-ordination. There may be mood swings or behavioural changes at specific times of the day and long term changes in personality or physical appearance. In the case of drugs, even the most experienced observer may have difficulty in identifying abuse and this may not be detected until the abuser is seriously affected. The best that a supervisor can hope for is to identify a course of conduct that is interfering with the employee's ability to function properly and to perform at his optimum potential.

People who use drugs or alcohol often behave differently from non-users and this difference can be measured by observation and with the aid of carefully maintained records. The DEA Guidelines have listed some indicators that may be helpful, there are many others. Drug or alcohol-abusing employees in the USA have been shown to: -

- Be late for work 3 times more often;

- Request early dismissal or time off 2.2 times more often;

- Use 3 times more sick leave;

- Be 5 times more likely to file worker compensation claims;

- Be 3.6 times more likely to have an accident at work and 9 times more likely to have a domestic or vehicle accident away from work;

- Have inconsistent work quality and lower productivity;

- Make more mistakes and have errors of judgement;

- Have mood swings that, over several days, seem to occur at similar times of the day;

- Be overly reactive to supervisory admonishments and compliments;

- Deliberately avoid co-workers and supervisors;

- Have deteriorating personal appearance, hygiene and ability to get along with co-workers;

- Invoke poor morale and reduced productivity among co-workers as a result of their "covering" for the abuser or their frustration with management ignorance or inaction to what they perceive to be an obvious drug and/or alcohol problem;

- Take needless risks in an attempt to raise productivity after supervisory admonishment;

- Handle and maintain machinery, equipment and supplies, carelessly;

- Disregard co-workers' safety;

- Increasingly complain about problems at home etc;

- Have frequent and recurring financial problems, including borrowing from others.

The HSE Booklet suggests the following symptoms may be indicators of possible drug abuse, they may be caused by other factors such as stress: -

- Sudden mood changes;

- Unusual irritability or aggression;

- A tendency to become confused;

- Abnormal fluctuations in concentration and energy;

- Impaired job performance;

- Poor time-keeping;

- Increased short-term sickness absence;

- A deterioration in relationships with colleagues, customers or management;

- Dishonesty and theft (arising from the need to maintain an expensive habit).

It is important that only those supervisors who have had specific and validated training be permitted to take direct action. Inexperienced and untrained supervisors should discuss any concerns that they may have with a qualified or senior supervisor. It is also important to remember that the majority of the workforce is drug free and does not abuse alcohol; they will be supportive of fair and even-handed policies aimed at ensuring that their workplace is not affected by drug and alcohol abuse/misuse.

CHAPTER 8
Education.

During the 1990's, the availability of dangerous drugs in the U.K. increased, to such a point that almost any person who wished to acquire anything from cannabis to crack cocaine had little difficulty in locating a supplier and, in most cases, the price was affordable. The Criminal Justice System had failed to bring about a widespread reduction in demand and had failed to discourage the suppliers and dealers from extending their activities. Coincidentally, a culture of tolerance and acceptance among the younger generation became widespread.

Britain was going through a similar, but less severe experience to that which had occurred in the United States of America in the previous two decades. The warnings had been clear but the "denial syndrome" was stronger and people did not want to believe that drugs would take such a strong hold on young people. Attitudes and mindsets were so strong that determined action against the epidemic was neglected.

Many official reports were written, and seminars paid lip service to the growing problem, but political action was insufficient. In less than ten years the problems that had engulfed others overtook the UK to such an extent that it developed one of the worst records in Europe for drug misuse and large scale dependency. No school is free from the effects of drugs and no child is likely to grow up free from that exposure.

There had been reluctance on the part of some influential people, to acknowledge that there was a growing problem because they thought that to admit to difficulties was an invitation to blame and the destruction of reputations and careers.

In the face of irrefutable evidence, some head teachers were refusing to acknowledge that their pupils consumed alcohol or had access to cannabis. The most that some would accept was "the odd cigarette behind the bicycle sheds" and there was a false logic prevailing that to talk about something like drugs was to encourage its use. In the former Central Region of Scotland, the Regional Council banned all head teachers from attending a seminar on the drug problem in the area in 1986 for exactly that reason. The Scottish Minister responsible for Education said on a television programme that it was wrong to speak to primary school pupils about drugs and that it would never be Government policy to do so

Within ten years, that became the policy but, in the meantime, much ground had been lost and those in favour of drug use and legalisation had been conducting a very effective and largely unopposed campaign. Indeed, it became received wisdom even with some members of the Government, that legalisation would take the profit out of drugs and would save the huge amounts of money being 'wasted' within the Criminal Justice System because of drug associated crime.

Ignorance about drugs and the nature of the drug problem was and remains widespread. Even the education programmes in some instances were tainted by a liberal approach which promoted the philosophy of allowing pupils to make "informed choices", when the emphasis should have been that to choose drugs is wholly wrong and harmful not only to self but to society in general. In some cases, pupils were being told how to use drugs "safely".

Discussions with teachers in Sydney, Australia, in 2002 revealed despair that police officers had given up on the prohibition message and had succumbed to the harm minimisation philosophy by informing pupils that if they choose to take drugs then there are relatively safe ways of doing so. Some people who favour the legalisation of drugs have advocated a similar approach to drug education in Australia in the UK.

The report of the Home Affairs Select Committee of the House of Commons in May 2002 {The Government's Drug Policy: Is it working? HC 318-1} drew attention to the fact that some of the education packages in UK schools were unsatisfactory and recommended that all education messages should be based upon the premise that any drug use can be harmful and should be discouraged. Indeed the report went on to criticise some leaflets by two government funded charities, which in its view had "crossed the line" between providing accurate information about drugs and encouraging young people to experiment with them.

The "harm reduction" approach crept into the syllabus in such a way that prohibition messages were replaced by information on 'responsible' and 'safe' use of dangerous drugs, when there is no safe way to use illicit drugs. The "Just Say No" message, which was successful in the USA in the 1980's, has been ridiculed and the "War on Drugs" has been criticised as inappropriate. Some have argued, in part successfully, that education should be about drugs and not against drugs.

A 1988 paper presented at an International Conference on Drug Policy Reform in Maryland by British participants entitled "Drug Education: A Basis for Reform" (Pat O'Hare, Julian Cohen and Ian Clements) said – "young people's experimental drug use should be accepted as a fact. They should be supported to enable them to use drugs in a less dangerous way". No matter how sincere some "harm reduction" advocates may be, their opinions have been taken out of context and adopted in some government endorsed education programmes in such a way as to promote the view that after being properly informed, pupils should remain free to choose a drug using lifestyle.

An example of this irresponsible attitude was mentioned in the Home Affairs Select Committee Report. Drugscope – which describes itself as a leading UK drug charity, published a leaflet entitled "What and Why? : Cannabis" which it claimed was aimed at parents and drugs workers. The document gives detailed information on cannabis, how it is taken, and some of the effects. The leaflet does say that cannabis has some unpleasant effects but goes on to list some pleasurable effects:-

> "Cannabis alters perception. The sensation is usually a pleasant one of general relaxation, a sense of being on the same wavelength as others who are 'stoned', and heightened sensitivity to colour and sound. Also common are the urge to eat ("the munchies") and fits of giggles as ordinary things become funny".

The leaflet continues by implying that many people regard using cannabis as a normal and socially enhancing activity.

Nevertheless, drug education has been acknowledged as an important tool in a young person's armoury and in his introduction to a Department for Education and Employment publication "Protecting Young People – Good practice in drug education in schools and the youth service." (1998) The Secretary of State for Education stated that education had become a cornerstone in the Government's 10 year Anti-Drugs Strategy 'Tackling Drugs to build a Better Britain' and that "Drug education needs to be embedded in the curriculum". In November 2000, the Secretary of State for Education announced an increase in spending on drug education in schools from £7.5million to £17.5million by 2003.

In 2001, the Home Office announced that the Government had commissioned a long-term study on the impact of drug, alcohol, and tobacco education in schools. This was a joint project between the Department for Education and Skills, the Department of Health and the Home Office. The study was to examine which types of educational input and other factors, such as socio-economic and cultural, have most impact on influencing behaviour. It was hoped that the study would take account of the criticism of the type of material that has been made available and the fact that a culture of tolerance and acceptance of drugs has taken hold in society, even amongst those who have no wish to take drugs themselves.

Of course, drug education was not entirely new and some very good and effective programmes had been developed over a number of years, but they were not comprehensively used and did not form the "cornerstone" referred to by the Secretary of State. Somewhat belatedly Government woke up to what should have been obvious and a great deal of work is now being undertaken to ensure that appropriate teaching is given within schools from primary through to senior level schools on a continuous basis.

The Aims and Objectives of Education.

According to the World Drug Report 2000 published by the United Nations Office for Drug Control and Crime Prevention, the majority of drug users have been introduced to substance misuse during their school years and often within the precincts of their schools. Education about drugs has formed part of many school programmes at all stages.

In the early years the syllabus may address a general discussion about hazardous products, in middle years much teaching should be aimed at the prevention elements that delay initial use of alcohol and tobacco products, and at deterring the illicit use of drugs. At the end of the school year the contents should address caution against dangerous practices and the problems that can arise from the abuse of mind-altering substances such as unsafe sex, binge drinking and drug cocktails.

Schools based prevention has been well researched and current evidence supports an approach which involves both pupils and their parents and which is evidenced based towards the promotion of health and well-being. The teaching should involve the pupils in a stimulating and positive experience and should:

- "be designed to enhance protective factors and attempt to reverse or reduce known risk factors;

- target all forms of drug abuse, including tobacco, alcohol, cannabis and solvents;

- include skills to resist drugs when offered; strengthen personal commitments not to use drugs; increase social competency (in communication, peer relationships, self efficacy and assertiveness);

- when targeted at adolescents, include interactive methods, such as peer discussion groups rather than didactic teaching techniques alone;

- include a component for parents or caregivers that reinforces what the children are learning, and that provides opportunities for family discussion;

- be long-term, taking place throughout the school career with repeat interventions to reinforce the original prevention goals;

- strengthen norms against drug use in all drug-abuse prevention settings (family, school, community);

- be adapted to address the specific nature of the drug-abuse problem in the local community;

- be more intensive and begin earlier the higher the level of risk experienced by the target population; and be age specific, developmentally appropriate, and sensitive to culture and gender" (World Drug Report 2000 at page 112).

It has to be remembered that the illicit drug trade is a massively profitable, tax free business run by ruthless organisations which have no compunctions about killing people to increase profits and which have such enormous spending power that corruption of officials is an easy and regular occurrence. Part of the marketing strategy is the publishing of false information about the effects of drugs which, if not countered by accurate information, will result in ill informed public opinion which, in turn, develops into a culture of tolerance and acceptance of drugs.

In addition to the criminal suppliers, there are others who have adopted a liberal attitude to drug use and who see it in terms of a matter of personal choice that should not be controlled by criminal justice sanctions. In pursuit of these beliefs, liberalisers and criminals have peddled much misinformation and pseudo research as evidence that laws should be abolished or relaxed.

A 'fatigue' has developed amongst some people to an extent where liberal views are being accepted at face value as an acceptable compromise in the face of a seemingly insoluble problem. Others have recognised that this hugely damaging and illegal activity cannot be defeated by law enforcement alone and that education to bring about demand reduction is as important as the criminal justice system. Readily available treatment is also a necessary adjunct to any successful drug strategy. It is also necessary to address the social problems and conditions, which contribute to some people resorting to drug use.

Education is a long-term commitment which aims to give people sufficient credible evidence so that they will reject drug abuse because they have decided for themselves it is the right thing to do and not because a teacher has told them that drug abuse is wrong. Naturally, the emphasis must be on educating young people who will become the parents and leaders of tomorrow. However, because of the widespread ignorance and misinformation that exists, it is also important to educate professional people and parents in particular and society in general, so that a totally supportive culture is able to back up what young people learn at school.

Research is demonstrating that young people generally are more influenced by their parents' attitudes, example, and opinions than has been acknowledged. (Shell Oil Company Research in American High Schools, 1999). "Establishment" adults are still suspect and by the time a child becomes a teenager it is likely that peer pressures may become a significant influence on the most vulnerable young people who may truant from school or run away from home, where it is harder to target them. Therefore, it is vitally important that parents are sufficiently well informed about the drug problem to enable them to discuss the matter confidently with their children before they become teenagers, instead of abdicating that responsibility by claiming that "children know more about drugs than we do". Of course, it is just as important to establish good communications with teenagers but it is better for secure foundations to be prepared early in the young person's life.

Research in the UK has shown that many children and young people are experiencing drugs at an increasingly earlier age. A large majority of young people never experiment with drugs. Nevertheless the impact of drugs on young lives is significant and it is likely that unless they are given a comprehensive education about the nature of drugs, they will adopt a dangerously, casual tolerance towards them because so many other people seem to use them freely.

According to the Report by Her Majesty's Chief Inspector of Schools in England & Wales, published in 1997 and entitled "Drug Education in Schools", effective teaching seeks both to increase pupils' knowledge and to encourage them to: -

- Improve their self-esteem.
- Make informed choices and decisions.
- Develop personal initiative and the ability to take responsibility.
- Recognise personal skills and qualities in themselves and others.
- Maintain and develop relationships.
- Develop self-confidence.
- Develop appropriate assertiveness.
- Develop the motivation to succeed.

These skills are seen to be particularly important in assisting children and young persons to deal with the pressures that they might face in a world where drugs are freely available. They are transferable skills which should be nurtured as part of the general 'skills for living' necessary for everyone; they are not related to drug education alone.

However, it should not be forgotten that for some people the idea of promoting "informed choices" is a device to encourage young people to experiment with drugs. The success of the "skills for living" approach depends upon the accuracy of the information given and the integrity and motivation of the teacher. All anti-drug education must be based on the understanding that illicit drug use is harmful and potentially, highly dangerous.

There should be no tolerance of any approach which might suggest that drug use is harmless fun.

The Education Reform Act 1988 (UK) specified that the curriculum in all maintained schools should promote "the spiritual, moral, cultural, mental and physical development of pupils at the school and of society" and should prepare them for "the opportunities, responsibilities and experiences of adult life".

Although Central Government in the UK had been slow to realise the importance of providing a comprehensive and continuous education process that would form a solid foundation in its campaign to reduce the acceptance of drugs, it did learn from experience elsewhere.

Most of the research into drug education has taken place in the USA, where for years there have been programmes targeting all levels of the education system from kindergarten through to high school. Of course, there were conflicting opinions and a certain amount of commercialism which claimed that one education package was better than another, but the consistent message was that education is vital and it is necessary to start teaching against illicit drugs as early as possible.

In 1986, the US Department of Education, under the guidance of the then Secretary of State, William J. Bennett, later to become a US Drug Czar, issued a booklet entitled "What Works – Schools without Drugs". This document drew together the experience and wisdom of educationists and researchers across the USA as advice for dealing with the growing drug problem in schools. Bennett said in his introduction: - "Knowing the dangers of drugs is not enough. Each of us must also act to prevent the sale and use of drugs. We must work to see that drug use is not tolerated in our homes, in our schools, or in our communities. Because of drugs, children are failing, suffering, and dying. We have to get tough, and we have to do it now".

The booklet drew attention to some interesting statistics and some pertinent observations on human nature in terms of "denial" and complacency. The first major comment was: -

> "Americans have consistently identified drug use among the top problems confronting the Nation's schools. Yet many do not recognise the degree to which their own children, their own schools, and their own communities are at risk."

The document drew attention to the facts that drug use was widespread among American children, the majority of whom obtained and used their drugs at school; that drug use affected all types of students and that initial use occurred at an increasingly earlier age. At that time (1986) it was estimated that one in six 13-year olds had used marijuana, and the greater a student's involvement with marijuana, the more likely it is the student will use other drugs in conjunction with marijuana. Once a child has accepted drugs the more difficult it becomes to change it's attitudes towards them, thus the best way to fight drug use is to begin prevention efforts before children start using drugs.

The role of parents was emphasised and the axiom that the teaching of standards of right and wrong and the demonstration of these standards in a consistent way in the home environment was endorsed. Parents were exhorted to: -

- Set a good example by not using drugs themselves;

- Explain to their children at an early age that drug use is wrong, harmful, and unlawful and reinforce this message throughout their adolescence;

- Encourage self-discipline through giving children everyday duties and holding them accountable for their actions;

- Establish standards of behaviour concerning drugs, drinking, dating, curfews, and unsupervised activities and enforce them consistently and fairly;

- Encourage children to stand by their convictions when pressured to use drugs.

These messages were in the context of the President and First Lady's campaign to "Just say No." which became so denigrated on both sides of the Atlantic in later years but which had been enormously successful at the time. Nevertheless, recognition of the problem and a remedy had occurred and the antidote was to be refined as the years passed.

Neither were the messages in 1986 as simplistic as appeared from the advice. A great deal of work had been carried out which had led educationists to conclude that schools should implement a comprehensive drug prevention curriculum from kindergarten through to grade 12, teaching that drug use is wrong and harmful and supporting the strengthening resistance to drugs. They proposed a model programme, which would have as main objectives: -

- To value and maintain sound personal health.

- To respect laws and rules prohibiting drugs.

- To resist pressures to use drugs.

- To promote student activities that are drug free and offer healthy avenues for student interests.

When developing a programme school staff should: -

- Determine curriculum content appropriate for the school's drug problem and grade levels.

- Base the curriculum on an understanding of why children try drugs in order to teach them how to resist pressures to use them.

- Review existing materials for possible adaptation.

When implementing the programme school staff members were encouraged to: -

- Include all grades because effective education is cumulative.

- Teach about drugs in health education classes, and reinforce this curriculum with appropriate materials in other classes such as social studies and science.

- Develop expertise in drug prevention through training.

- Teachers should be knowledgeable about drugs, be personally committed to opposing drug use, and be skilled at eliciting participation by students.

Schools were also encouraged to enlist the aid of the community in terms of support and assistance by developing collaborative projects in which school personnel, parents, school boards, police, other social organisations and private groups could work together to provide the necessary resources and back-up.

The Life Skills approach.

As the drug problem engulfed America and it became obvious that law enforcement alone could not overcome it, many people turned to education to help bring about "demand reduction". In addition to the "Just Say No" initiatives taken by the First Lady, Nancy Reagan, in the 1980s, a number of organisations developed education programmes for use in the schools.

Several of the national programmes, particularly those sponsored by the Drug Enforcement Administration, used prominent athletes as role models for the nation. A number of athletes made a public stand against drug abuse and throughout the High Schools, coaches were trained to encourage and promote the message of healthy living and drug free sport. Sport was identified as one of the many alternatives to drug abuse. Ironically, the deaths of two prominent athletes – Len Bias and Don Rogers – from drug overdoses were incidents that helped to shock many people into the realisation that there is no such thing as safe and responsible use of illicit drugs.

Len Bias was a young, black basketball player with Boston Celtics who was on the verge of great wealth and national fame when he died from heart failure caused by cocaine poisoning. His death was particularly poignant because he was a member of a good living, religious family; he was not the stereotyped 'drop-out', with no prospects. The result of these deaths was that Americans began to realise that drug abuse respects no social or cultural boundaries

The DEA's Sports Drug Awareness Programme was run in conjunction with other organisations such as the National High School Athletic Coaches Association, the National Football League Players Association and the International Association of Chiefs of Police. The Administration made a total commitment to demand reduction through education. It appointed a full time Bureau Chief in Charge of such programmes. John C. Lawn the Administrator of the DEA and a former teacher himself said: "I believe that DEA's demand reduction programmes form a valuable, even vital, part of our mission".

The Administration also became involved in a range of activities with young people including the Law Enforcement Explorer Programme of the Boy Scouts of America. These programmes were used to encourage young people to use "positive peer pressure" to prevent others from becoming involved with drug experimentation. The aid of good and dedicated teachers was enlisted in developing programmes, which would help young people acquire the necessary skills to enable them to resist drugs.

Across America, many people came to realise that "life skills" were a vitally important part of education, which had not been refined and included universally in the school curriculum. It was recognised that social influences and pressures form a significant factor in persuading some young people to experiment with drugs. The child's desire to feel that he belongs to a group or to assert independence was acknowledged to be a normal part of the maturing process which needs to be supervised.

The general belief was that children have to be taught to recognise the pitfalls and be assisted to develop the strength of character and the social skills to resist improper influences. Progressively these messages were prepared for use in the schools and were recommended by the US Department of Education. Schools were encouraged to deal with the subject of drug abuse in a constructive and comprehensive manner by developing an anti-drug theme throughout the complete education experience.

In the booklet "What Works – Schools without Drugs" sample topics across the education spectrum were commended: -

- The influence of popular culture on behaviour.

- The influence of peers, parents and other important individuals on a student's behaviour. How the need to feel accepted by others influences behaviour.

- Ways to make responsible decisions and deal constructively with disagreeable moments and pressures.

- Reasons for not taking drugs.

- Situations in which students might feel pressurised into taking drugs.

- Ways of resisting pressure to use drugs.

- Benefits of resisting pressure to use drugs.

This list of suggested topics was reinforced by sample learning activities, which included: -

- Describe recent personal decisions. In small groups, decide what considerations influenced the decision (e.g. opinions of family or friends, beliefs, desire to be popular) and analyse choices and consequences.

- Examine advertisements for cigarettes, over-the-counter drugs, and alcohol, deciding what images are being projected and whether the advertisements are accurate.

- Read about famous people who stood up for their beliefs in the face of opposition. Students can discuss how these people withstood the pressure and what they accomplished.

- Give reasons for not taking drugs. Discuss with the health educator or drug counsellor the false arguments for using drugs. Develop counter-arguments in response.

- Given a scenario depicting pressure to use drugs, act out ways of resisting (simply refusing, giving a reason, leaving the scene etc.). Practice the techniques repeatedly. Demonstrate ways of resisting using older students, trained as 'peer' teachers.

- Present scenarios using drug related problems (e.g. learning that another student is selling drugs, a sibling using drugs; or being offered a lift by a friend under the influence of drugs/alcohol). Students practice what they would do and discuss to whom to turn for help. Teachers should discuss and evaluate the appropriateness of student responses.

- Discuss how it feels to resist pressures to take drugs. Hold a poster contest to depict the benefits derived from not using and saying no (e.g. being in control, increased respect from others, self-confidence).

It was almost a decade before a similar realisation and commitment became generally apparent within the UK education system. In 1995, the Department for Education and Employment issued a Circular entitled "Drug Prevention and Schools" (4/95). It began by acknowledging that drug misuse posed a major threat to individuals, families and the wider community and endorsed the Government strategy set out in the White Paper "Tackling Drugs Together" also issued in 1995. The Government's aims were declared to be 'to take effective action by vigorous law enforcement, accessible treatment and a new emphasis on education and prevention to:

- Increase the safety of communities from drug-related crime;
- Reduce the acceptability and availability of drugs to young people; and
- Reduce the health risks and other damage related to drug misuse'.

It was recognised that drug misuse is an educational issue and that education 'can play a key role in ensuring that young people know the risks of drug taking and have the knowledge and skills to resist'.

The Circular went on to make the point that schools alone could not "solve" the problem of drugs in society but an effective programme of drug education in schools is an important step in tackling it. It recognised that an effective programme of education included working in partnership with health, social services, police, and other agencies.

The Circular stated that similar teaching should be applied about alcohol, tobacco, and other volatile substances (solvents for inhalation). It acknowledged also that the available evidence (including that from the USA) indicated that the age of first use of drugs was falling and that the number of deaths resulting directly from drug misuse was rising. Reference was made to the 1992 British Crime Survey information on self reported drug use and findings published in a Home Office paper in 1995; and just as in America the conclusion was that − "Information and skills to resist drugs are best provided before exposure and experimentation are likely". The Circular also stated that − "Primary, and even nursery, school sites may be used after hours for drug misuse so even the youngest children may need to be warned of the dangers from discarded equipment".

In many ways the Circular was an enlightened document which contained all of the information and suggestions that had been available a decade before in the USA. It commended the practice of giving drug education as part of an integrated programme of health education, which should be built up over all of the stages of education. It emphasised that the essential aim underlying any programme should be "to give pupils the facts, emphasise the benefits of a healthy lifestyle, and give young people the knowledge and skills to make informed and responsible choices now and later on in life".

The necessity of schools responding to changing trends in drug misuse and of offering a credible, consistent and continuous message to pupils was noted.

Shock tactics were judged to be ineffective, as was teaching about drugs in an isolated lesson or in circumstances where drugs have been 'bolted on' to an existing topic. Clear warnings, backed up by evidence, of the dangerous effects of drugs were thought to be particularly powerful. Specific and carefully planned lessons were recommended as being better than a casual or oblique reference to drugs.

Always the danger of arousing an unhealthy interest or an inclination towards experimentation has to be considered. Any outside contribution to the anti-drug programme must be compatible with the policy and teaching of the school. Parental involvement was encouraged even to the point of providing teaching for parents to help them to recognise the signs of drug misuse and giving them information on where to turn for specialist help and advice.

In fact, all of the information contained in the Circular was designed to encourage education programmes, formal and written school policies about drugs, the involvement of parents, pupils and school governors in formulating those policies; and ways of dealing with drug related incidents in schools.

It is interesting to note that the Home Affairs Select Committee Report in 2002 disagreed with the idea that shock-tactics are necessarily counter-productive. Experience has indicated that as part of a carefully prepared information package, shocking images of the possible consequences of illicit drug misuse do have their place and are no more horrific than many of the fictional and factual representations on television. The initial objection to shock tactics stemmed from their being used as a blunt instrument, out of context and without either explanation or accurate information to accompany the images.

The place of Drug Education in the Curriculum.

Two years after the issue of DfEE Circular 4/95 the Ofsted Report

" Drug Education in Schools" issued its main findings. This report was prepared after targeted visits to 40 maintained primary schools and 80 maintained secondary schools. It included the analysis of data obtained from other formal inspections of primary and secondary schools, a questionnaire survey of 1500 schools, and additional information obtained from health and education professionals based outside schools, but associated with drug education.

An important conclusion was that many schools were able to raise pupils' awareness levels about drugs but it was unclear for how long pupils maintained this enhanced state of awareness.

Longer term 'follow-up' surveys would be necessary to establish this information and the schools have neither the resources nor the capability of doing this. Other findings were inconclusive but suggested that the teaching of values and personal skills "can result in improved parenting skills, especially family communication and self-esteem, although there were no direct relationships established with the prevention of drug misuse." Successes were claimed for programmes that train pupils to resist pressures to take drugs and for the credibility of 'peer education programmes', which gave young people the opportunity to gain information about drugs which they regarded as credible. It was thought that these programmes could also assist in the development of skills needed to resist drug taking

It is not surprising that there was little evidence available to Ofsted about the long term impact of drug education programmes as a result of their own researches. The North American experience, over many years had placed great store on the efficacy of teaching life skills, and there is plenty of literature available to support that thinking. The same misgivings must be applicable to many areas of education, and even if there is a 'homespun logic' about teaching transferable skills, common sense must indicate that such training has to be beneficial. A pragmatic and realistic approach must be adopted as a matter of urgency, drawing on UK research as and when it becomes available.

The main findings of the report were: -

- Pupils' knowledge about drugs was at least satisfactory and often good and the majority of pupils are taught the skills needed to resist when offered drugs.

- At Key Stage 1 (5-7 years) the majority understand the value of drugs as medicines; recognise dangers associated with unknown substances, and are aware of associated safety issues concerning who can give them medicine

- At Key Stage 2 (7-11 years) improved knowledge of drugs but focuses on those things thought most likely to affect them – namely alcohol and tobacco. At this stage, pupils are given the opportunity to reflect on their own attitudes towards the use of drugs and develop a range of strategies for when drugs are offered.

- At Key Stage 3 (11-14 years) and 4 (14-16 years) programmes assist in broadening and deepening knowledge. Pupils benefit from being given time to develop their own relevant skills.

- The quality of teaching is good in over 60% of lessons and satisfactory in a further 25%. The poorest teaching was found to be at stage 3 where it was most frequently associated with tutorials and where some teachers lacked the necessary knowledge and skills.

- Too many schools failed to assess pupils' knowledge and understanding of drugs, before planning and implementation of programmes. After teaching, assessment of knowledge and skills was not made in many cases.

- Where teaching was across the curriculum often there was a lack of co-ordination resulting in loss of overall coherence.

- Overall, drug education through the personal and social education (PSE) programme is more coherent and effective than through the tutorial system.

- Schools were not taking monitoring and evaluation of drug education programmes sufficiently seriously, particularly concerning the quality of teaching.

- Evaluation of the long-term effects of drug education on the behaviour of individuals lies beyond the resources of individual schools and Local Education Authorities.

"Protecting Young People"

This 1998 document built on the Ofsted Report and identified areas of good practice in drug education in both schools and the youth service. It highlighted the conclusion that drug education is most successfully delivered as part of a personal, social and health education curriculum. Programmes should emphasise accurate information, social skills, approaches such as peer pressure resistance, as well as improvement in self-awareness and self-esteem. They should be based on a sustained, long-term approach and curriculum building on previously established foundations, which address accurately the pupils' needs at each stage of their development.

The programme should include a variety of teaching methods such as feed back, role-playing, and skills-rehearsal in addition to knowledge and information. The document emphasises that schools should: -

- Appoint a co-ordinator;
- Draw up and regularly review a policy document in consultation with parents, pupils, school governors and other relevant bodies with drug knowledge such as LEA's, police, and drug agencies.

Drawing heavily on references in American literature, the document states that by targeting primary schools it is possible to delay the onset of the age at which some children will experiment with or first use a substance, whether drugs, alcohol, tobacco or solvents.

- This is valuable because a relationship has been established between early use and long-term problems and delay and non-dependent behaviour. In fact research in the USA has indicated that if a young person does not smoke before reaching the age of 18 years it is likely that he will not do so in adult life. A similar logic applies to the misuse of drugs and providing a person has not become accustomed to the misuse of drugs by the age of 21 years, then it is likely that he will not do so at all.

- Notwithstanding the observation in the 1997 Ofsted Report that no direct relationship had been established between teaching social skills and a reduction in drug use, the 1998 publication "Protecting Young People" devoted a section to Life Skills approaches in drug education. It appears to endorse this method as a credible and worthwhile teaching strategy in helping to protect young people against the dangers of pressures to use drugs. Whatever the correlation between such teaching methods and a reduction in drug activity among young people, it is obvious that it is better to give this type of training in the context of a great social risk rather than to expect young people to develop their own defence mechanisms unaided. The document makes the point: - "Such approaches can build on more traditional life skills programmes and effectively complement activities intended to enhance self-esteem, communication skills, values clarification and decision making".

- The assumption behind such programmes is that if young people are able to see that the skills they have acquired enable them to perform well and skilfully in their own accepted environment they will find this rewarding. If they cannot, they may seek approval in an alternative society with different values, which approves of anti-social behaviour including the misuse of alcohol and drugs.

- Unfortunately, when the document deals with the role of Youth Services in drug education, it draws attention to the lack of co-ordination and points out some confusion about appropriate responses to young people. Endorsement is given to "harm minimisation" programmes as being the most likely to be the most effective. Such approval gives rise to concern and the criticism that by adopting such an approach there is a mixed message which might lead some young people to conclude that taking drugs cannot be so dangerous if 'official' guidance is being offered on how to "do drugs" safely and responsibly.

The Harm Reduction/minimisation message in the context of Education

A report from America draws attention to changing attitudes in the classrooms in which - "Approaches that are less didactic, more child-centred, more promotive of "children's rights" have been promoted in the schools. The authority of teachers has been diminished just as it has been with parents. The focus in education has shifted from one of compliance with societal boundaries to one of leaving pupils to make "informed choices". That "informing" is being shaped by liberals who, in many cases, condone drug use".

('The Harm Reduction Invasion of Drug Prevention Education'
- C. Fay, Drug Free America Foundation, June 1999.)

In this context Harm-Reduction advocates assume that children and young people are going to use illegal drugs and therefore, rather than teaching them not to use illegal drugs, it is better to teach them how to use them in a 'responsible' and 'safe' manner.

Apparently, the shift towards harm reduction was first noticed in North America in the late 1980s when supporters of liberal drug policy began publishing articles and holding International Conferences under the title of 'Harm Reduction'. It has been noted already that there is no universal definition of the term; it is usual for it to be applied to a situation where actual drug misuse has already occurred. The extension into the formal education system on the premise that drugs are available to children and that some of them will use them at some time seems to be stretching a point.

In the introduction to a booklet entitled 'The Harm Reduction Model' by Diane Riley, published in Canada in 1994 by the Harm Reduction Network, the point is made that the advice contained in it is intended for drug users and their service providers. "It (the booklet) is not intended to judge users, nor to promote drug use, but to inform, help, support and protect".

The 'Harm Reduction' model is traced back to the recommendations of a British Report prepared in the 1920s by the Rolleston Committee, in which a group of leading physicians concluded that in certain cases maintenance on drugs may be necessary to help users lead useful lives.

Riley states that the re-emergence of 'Harm Reduction' as a social policy in the 1990s was because of an increase in the number of users who were injecting drugs. The dangers associated with this practice, which include the spread of blood borne diseases such as Aids and Hepatitis C were thought to be a key reason for promoting safe methods of taking drugs. The author does mentions that a number of countries and organisations, including the World Health Organisation, have adopted 'Harm Reduction' in a health context, as both policy and practice, for that reason.

Canada adopted 'Harm Reduction' as the framework for its National Drug Strategy (CDS.) in 1987. The Canadian Government defined harm as "sickness, death, social misery, crime, violence and economic costs to all levels of government". No mention is made of introducing this approach into schools, but in 1992 an article appeared in "The Journal" in Canada by Julian Cohen in which the author said: -

> "Primary prevention tools… are unsuccessful because they suggest, incorrectly, that drug use is abnormal for young people. There is nothing abnormal about it. Harm reduction education is about drugs.
>
> The primary prevention approach ignores the fun, the pleasure, the benefits, of drug use. It is important that we understand quite clearly that drug use is purposeful, drug use is fun for young people, and drug use brings benefits to them. Harm reduction is not aimed at stopping young people from using drugs … it has a different philosophy and ideology from abstinence or primary prevention. Drug use is a normal human activity and there is nothing abnormal about it. Harm reduction education is about drugs…it is non-judgmental… one of the principles is that we respect young people's rights to make their own decisions."

It is this approach to 'Harm Reduction', which causes much concern to those who believe that the primary aim of education in the school setting should be to teach that drug misuse is unacceptable and dangerous. It is important to keep up to date with information about drugs particularly in schools education packs. It should be incumbent on those responsible for Inspecting schools to ensure that well intentioned statements about enabling pupils to make "informed choices" are not misconstrued or manipulated into meaning something totally different from abstinence. The message in all school curricula must be to encourage abstinence and not to risk confusing pupils with intentional or unintentional suggestions that allow "informed choices" to include the belief that drug taking is risk free.

Clearly, harm reduction has a place in a medical context where the aim is to prevent the spread of diseases or unwanted pregnancies. It is questionable whether such a philosophy is entirely appropriate in a schools education context where, of course it is important to minimise the harm to young and impressionable pupils, but not by teaching or implying, that illicit drug taking is acceptable if done 'safely'. The key, message in schools must be abstinence and this was reinforced by the Home Affairs Select Committee Report on Government Drug Policy in 2002. The Annual Report of the International Narcotics Control Board for 2003 emphasised the point that "Harm Reduction" approaches should not be seen to condone or promote drug abuse but should contribute to a reduction in the abuse of drugs leading to total abstinence.

(INCB 2003 United Nations)

Drugs: Guidance for Schools

Early in 2004, the Department for Education and Skills in England issued a new document (DfES/0092/2004), which replaced the circular 4/95: Drug Prevention and Schools and Protecting Young People: good practice in drug education and the youth service (1998). This new document offers guidance on all matters relating to drug education, the management of drugs within the school community, supporting the needs of pupils about drugs and drug policy development. It addresses both licit and illicit drugs as well as alcohol, tobacco, and volatile substances used for inhalation.

The essential message in this document is that all schools should offer a drug education programme that is developmental and appropriate to the age, maturity, and ability of all pupils. The thrust of the message is that drug education should be delivered as part of personal, social and health education (PSHE) and citizenship. There is stress on the need for education programmes to take account of pupils' views and existing knowledge and understanding. Teachers who are skilled, confident, and knowledgeable about drugs should deliver the lessons and must emphasise that the possession, use or supply of illegal and other unauthorised drugs within school boundaries is unacceptable. The overall emphasis of the teaching should be that the abuse of drugs should not occur.

There is a requirement that all schools should develop and publish a drug policy, which sets out the school's role and function in relation to all drug matters and a senior member of staff should be designated as the person having overall responsibility for this. There is stress on the need for the policy to be developed in consultation with all that have a legitimate interest in the school, especially pupils and their parents/carers. All actions, responsibilities, and procedures relating to drugs should be clearly understood by the whole school community and this should be fully documented and revised on a regular basis.

A vital piece of advice is that all school staff should receive drug awareness training and should understand the policy and their responsibilities within it. Clear referral protocols with a range of relevant agencies should be established in the case of any pupils who may be particularly vulnerable to drug misuse either personally or within their home environment.

Drug Testing within Schools.

The random testing of school pupils for drugs and alcohol has been common throughout the USA for a number of years and the Supreme Court has endorsed this practice. In his State of the Union address in January 2004 the US President called for an additional $23 million of Federal funds to encourage drug testing in those schools that wanted to use it as a tool to reduce the demand for illicit drugs. The funding was proposed as part of a community based strategy aimed at educating and not punishing children.

Coincidentally the Drug Free Education Act 2004 was introduced the purpose of which was to:

- Educate school administrators about the advantages of a drug-free school and how random drug testing can help achieve this goal.

- Provide grants and technical assistance to Local Education Agencies to help enable the development and implementation of student drug testing programmes that suit individual needs.

- Assist school districts in utilising funding available through a Safe and Drug Free Schools Programme for student drug testing programmes.

The Programmes must include:

- A written policy which includes a clear statement of expectations for school behaviour, prohibitions against attending school or school activities under the influence of illegal drugs or alcohol, prohibition against the possession or use of illegal drugs in school, and the consequences of violating those expectations and prohibitions.

- Student access to student assistance programme, including confidential assessment, referral, and short-term problem resolution.

- Drug and alcohol abuse prevention training for all students and staff.

- Random student drug testing, with analysis conducted by an approved laboratory.

All drug-testing records must be:

- kept strictly confidential
- Require the use of a Medical Review Officer for all confirmed positive results

- Exclude law enforcement notification of school results

- Be destroyed upon student graduation or transfer from the school district

At the beginning of every school year, all parents must be notified of their right to withdraw their child from participation in the random drug-testing programme.

Experience in some American schools has shown that a testing programme has been particularly helpful to pupils who wish to resist peer pressure to use illegal substances especially for those who wish to participate in sports or other school activities. The ban gives pupils a legitimate reason to resist pressure to use drugs that does not expose them to ridicule. However, testing can be a severe drain on school funds and is not universally popular because there have been reports that testing regimes have not always achieved the desired result of a decrease in the use of drugs and alcohol.

Research has shown that if people can be prevented from using drugs and alcohol during their early years before achieving their majority then it is unlikely that they will become dependent abusers. However, the reverse is also true and because young bodies and minds are immature, the potential for harm by the abuse of drugs and alcohol at an early age is increased significantly. All current research stresses the dangers of drug misuse to the young.

Whilst it may be true currently that the abuse of drugs in the UK is not as far advanced as in some American States there is little doubt that the problem is worsening. With one of the worst drug abuse records in Europe, the UK cannot afford to be complacent. The random testing of pupils for the use of drugs is considered by some to be a useful tool in securing demand reduction, giving pupils a legitimate reason for resisting peer pressure to use drugs, and providing a catalyst to bring about a greater awareness of the dangers of drugs. The Prime Minister made a statement in March 2004 that he would introduce powers for Head Teachers to introduce drug testing for pupils.

Drug Education in Schools ~ Ofsted Report 2005.

This report was issued in July 2005 and was based on evidence gathered from over 60 schools visited and 200 school inspection reports. It concluded that the majority of young people of school age have never used an illegal drug although it anticipated that some would inevitably experiment but that most would not go on to become problem drug users. While conceding that every school has a responsibility to consider its response to drugs it stated ~ "the key aim of drug education is to make healthy informed choices" when most concerned parents would probably assert that the key aim should be to teach that the abuse of all drugs is dangerous and should not even be considered. However, the report did go on to say that as with most aspects of personal, social and health education (PSHE) the expectations of drug education are that, as well as increasing knowledge, changing attitudes and enhancing skills, the teaching should also impact positively on pupils' behaviour but in isolation a school drug education programme cannot achieve these targets.

The Report concluded that since the previous Ofsted assessment in 1997 there had been a marked improvement in the quality of planning of drug education programmes, achievement was noted to be higher at all stages and that most schools had effective plans for dealing with drug related incidents. It noted that pupils were more concerned to be informed about alcohol and tobacco, which were perceived to have greater potential health risks for them. Some of the key findings were: ~

- The more effective lessons should challenge pupils' attitudes and help them develop a range of skills such as decision making and assertiveness;

- Whilst the quality of teaching had continued to improve in some schools insufficient learning time was provided, and up to date specialist knowledge had not been acquired;

- Assessment of results was poor and policies were dated in some instances;

- A lack of awareness of pupils' needs was apparent in many schools;

- Some schools did not back up education with access to adult support that pupils felt met confidentiality needs;

- Most schools had attempted to involve parents but information and advice evenings attracted little support/interest and some parents fail in their responsibilities;

- Most schools indicated that their policies for dealing with drugs would not include random drug testing

Recommendations:-

Apart from putting right the deficiencies identified in the key findings, the report suggested that some national bodies in drug education should consider -

- There needs to be a comprehensive evaluation of the effectiveness of drug education programmes used in schools;

- There is a need to subject both drug testing programmes and the use of sniffer dogs to rigorous and independent evaluation;

- Training and resources need to be made available to parents to enable them to play a greater role in advising and supporting their children and they should be encouraged to make use of them.

CHAPTER 9
International Action to reduce Drug Trafficking.

Despite the enormity of the task of reducing the world-wide demand for drugs and that of preventing illicit drug manufacturing and trafficking, there have been some major successes internationally in countering the narcotics industry. To the ordinary persons in the street this task may seem to be impossible. The persuasive arguments of the "legalisers" become attractive and it may seem easier to accept the reality of drugs than to oppose them. This lends support to the traffickers who wish to continue to ply their trade as easily as possible. Such pessimism has no place in dealing with a hugely damaging and dangerous problem.

At the beginning of the twenty first century combined international efforts have made inroads into the drug syndicates' fields of operation although much more remains to be done. The activities of drug cartels have been interrupted and fragmented by determined and more effective law enforcement. Precursor chemicals have been prevented from falling into the hands of the illicit manufacturers. Transportation routes have been disrupted, forcing the traffickers to seek alternative, more expensive methods of delivering their products but still the damaging trade appears to be thriving despite statistics that are produced to indicate a decline in demand. Of course there have been major successes but the nature of the problem is that governments cannot afford to ease up on their anti-drug policies otherwise, like a Hydra headed monster, it breaks out repeatedly.

Improvements in judicial systems, law enforcement, investigative methods, and better extradition arrangements have denied criminals places of safety. Closer international co-operation between governments and financial institutions has made money-laundering more difficult and costly so that it has become extremely difficult for the drug syndicates to legitimise their profits. Confiscated assets have been used in the fight against the drug trade. Crop eradication and alternative development programmes have been established in drug producing regions, and these measures have made an impact on the total availability of drugs although there have been some difficulties which have still to be addressed. However, for every success, there is usually a counter measure by the drug syndicates and each day new markets and increased demands are made for illicit drugs which the drug lords are anxious to accommodate and which require even more determined resistance.

Long-term strategies.

In 2003 the UN conducted its mid-term review of progress following UNGASS in 1998 and noted some particularly beneficial achievements.

First internationally accepted standards to reduce demand for illicit drugs had been reflected in the Declaration on Guiding Principles of Demand Reduction where before the concentration had been on supply. This had resulted in a balanced approach in all operations, with new emphasis being placed on prevention, advocacy and treatment.

Secondly UNGASS had put a new emphasis on building instruments to measure the evolution of the drug problem, thereby building a more reliable evidence base for assessing the impact of policy.

Thirdly UNGASS had set out requirements for Governments, and for the UN, to ensure objective evaluation of policies, programmes and projects.

There is no short-term remedy that will solve the problem of drugs overnight. Many take the view that the most that can be achieved would be a major reduction in the demand for drugs and a combined international, political will to proscribe illicit drugs. Their use and abuse should reduce and should become more of a medical than a law-enforcement problem. Underlying most advanced thinking on the drug issue is an acknowledgement that international drug control strategies must be continuous and long-term.

They must have a profound effect in changing attitudes, cultures, and the thinking in the key, national institutions of the main drug source and transit countries. They must also have an equally profound effect in educating consumers and potential consumers of their devastating effects. The more enlightened countries are trying to bring about positive influence by helping governments to modernise their legal and judicial systems and to make their law enforcement agencies more professional. Without the integrity and professionalism that are essential to effective counter-narcotics measures in all developed countries, the task of preventing drug trafficking will become almost impossible.

Dishonest or 'frightened' judges can frustrate the efforts of the most dedicated law enforcement agencies and too powerful and wealthy drug lords can overcome democratic institutions by a rule of terror, corruption, and death. It takes time, courage, and dedication to bring about the healthy transformation of an institutionally corrupt and drug dependent country into a stable and well-motivated democracy. The education process must be continuous, accurate, and relevant.

The reasons why people are persuaded to consume vast amounts of 'mind-altering' substances must be addressed. The International Conventions against drugs have set out the ways in which drug trafficking may be inhibited. Many countries have signed-up to these agreements, but their effectiveness depends upon honesty of intention and active implementation and it is important that they are kept under review and updated to address modern conditions.

Either because of a lack of political wills, the necessary level of determination, or because of the state of development in some countries these measures are not yet as successful, universally as the original planners hoped that they might be. Nevertheless, an enormous amount of progress is being made and it would be unwise to abandon these initiatives simply because international criminal gangs have the resources and the determination to advance their pernicious trade.

Unfortunately, the resistance to drug abuse in some countries has weakened and a culture of tolerance and acceptance has developed such that several European countries have, effectively, decriminalised possession and use of the so-called 'soft' drugs such as cannabis. An international initiative in support of the legalisation of drugs has gained ground under the slogan -"The war on drugs has been lost".

Such changes in policy have been fragmented and have sent out mixed messages to a largely uninformed public, which are conveying the general impression that "responsible" drug use is not very harmful and are no worse than the use of tobacco or alcohol. Effectively this attitude has caused some governments to "take their eye off the ball" and instead of investing in continuous and long-term supply and demand reduction strategies, with treatment where necessary, they have allowed liberal policies to almost encourage drug use.

A similar situation arose in the USA after the very successful "Just Say No" campaign sponsored by the Reagan Administration, became neglected out of a sense of complacency. The Government of the day thought that its policies were so successful that it was not necessary to keep on with succeeding generations with the result that drug abuse began to rise at an alarming rate. Instead of identifying past successes there was a change of policy, which almost succumbed to the rhetoric about wasted resources and lost wars. There must be a universal recognition that opposition to drug abuse must be a permanent feature of all governments' policies. It is unlikely to be possible to say that the problem of illicit drugs has been overcome.

International Narcotics Control Strategy – USA.

The leading country in the fight against drugs, in terms of the amount of money invested and the international actions that are taken, is the USA. The Department of State's Bureau of International Narcotics and Law Enforcement Affairs (INL) is responsible for managing a huge budget for narcotics control and anti-crime assistance to foreign countries.
Until the financial year of 2002, under the terms of the Foreign Assistance Act of 1961 (as amended), the President of the United States followed a certification procedure in which major illicit drug producing and/or major illicit drug transit countries are

identified. A certificate was issued if they had co-operated fully with the United States or had taken adequate steps of their own, to achieve full compliance with the goals and objectives of the 1988 United Nations Convention Against Illicit Traffic in Narcotic Drugs and Psychotropic Substances.

In other circumstances a certificate could have been issued if it was deemed to be in "the vital national interests of the United States" to do so. Only two countries in these categories were denied certificates in 2000 – Afghanistan and Burma. Myanmar (Burma) was again criticised in 2005 for failing to take appropriate action against drug production.

The purpose of these certificates was twofold. Firstly certification enabled receipt of development and military assistance from the US Government; foreign governments that did not meet the necessary standards lost eligibility for most forms of assistance and they faced a mandatory "no" vote by the US Government on loans in six multilateral development banks. Secondly, the US Government used the certification process as a means of focusing "an international spotlight on corruption".

Drug trafficking and the corruption that goes with it thrives on secretiveness and underhand conspiracies. By exposing those countries which failed to live up to the standards set in the UN Conventions the United States pursued a controversial but, as it saw it, a very effective method of encouraging compliance.

In 2002 a new certification process was introduced for countries on a list of major illicit drug producing or drug-transit countries. In lieu of the certification procedures described above, section 591 of the Foreign Assistance Act now requires the President to submit a report no later than 45 days after the Act is enacted (annually) that identifies each country that the President has determined to be a major drug transit or major drug producing country. The President is also required in that report to identify any country on the majors list that has "failed demonstrably...to make substantial efforts" during the previous 12 months to adhere to international counternarcotics agreements and to take certain counternarcotics measures set forth in US law. However, if the President determines that the provision of assistance is vital to US national interests or that the country, at any time after the President's initial report to Congress, has made "substantial efforts" to comply with the counternarcotics conditions in the legislation, then assistance may be provided. The prohibition does not apply to humanitarian and certain other types of assistance. The Foreign Relations Authorization Act of 2003 made permanent law the modifications described above.

Each year the US Government issues its 'International Narcotics Control Strategy Report' (INSCR) as a form of what it describes as 'public diplomacy'. The Report is seen as a powerful policy instrument which stresses openness and transparency and which makes every government concerned with the certification process, publicly accountable for its actions – including the United States itself. The goal of this procedure is not so much a sanction process but rather a means of encouraging a common and internationally acknowledged standard of co-operation.

Measures of Success.

Despite the obstacles and the increasing efficiency of the international criminal organisations in promoting the drug trade the United States points to some significant successes in its action against drugs:

- Steady decline in the Andean Coca Crop. Despite an upsurge in production in Colombia by 20% in 1999 and more efficient processing methods for cocaine, overall there has been a decline in the Andean coca crop when compared with 1987 when assessments were first made. The Governments of Bolivia and Peru have been active, with US assistance in pursuing the aims of the Special Session of the UN General Assembly in New York in 1998 of total eradication of illicit drug crops. Of the 115,300 hectares under cultivation in Peru in 1995 only 38,700 remained in 1999 – a drop of two thirds. During the same 4-year period in Bolivia, the Government crop eradication programme cut coca cultivation by more than half – from 48,600 to 21,800 hectares. However, it was widely reported in February 2001 than there has been a reversal of the early successes in crop-eradication programmes, particularly in Peru. Reports emanating from UNDCP indicated that raw coca prices had doubled and farmers were returning to the abandoned coca fields. In November 2000, demonstrations by Peruvian farmers forced the Government to abandon its eradication programme.

Footnote:- (Coca Makes Big Comeback in Bolivia As Alternative Crops Fail. The Wall Street Journal (5/12, Lifsher) reports, "The U.S.'s long-successful war on drugs in Bolivia, the world's third-biggest producer of coca, is running into serious trouble. To understand why, look at this isolated hamlet, where for more than a decade farmer Pastor Torrico was a loyal ally of the U.S. When men from the U.S. Agency for International Development first came here in the late 1980s, he agreed to uproot his few acres of coca bushes, whose oval green leaves provide the main ingredient of cocaine. At the Americans' urging, Mr. Torrico plunged into legal cash crops. He attended a training program in Costa Rica, borrowed money to buy seedlings and equipment, and planted macadamia trees. But the trees never produced their delicate white nuts, and Mr. Torrico had to sell his house in 1990 to pay off his loan. Subsequent attempts to raise palm hearts and oranges also 'were total losses,' he says. The whole crop-substitution program put him off Americans. He went back to raising a little coca, an increasingly difficult business given the government's coca-eradication crusade of recent years. Now the 60-year-old farmer is a foot soldier, along with tens of thousands of other disgruntled peasants, for a fiercely anti-American socialist named Evo Morales. ... With startling speed, much of a nation the U.S. touts as a leader in the war on drugs is just saying no to Washington. Illegal coca cultivation is on the rise after dropping 90% between 1998 and 2001, according to U.S. estimates. ... Bolivian government officials say they're considering a study of the commercial viability of expanding legal coca. But Washington opposes legalization. The Bush administration is already fretting that Bolivian coca production rose 23% last year from its low point in 2001 because of rapid replanting.")

In December 2005 Evo Morales was elected President of Bolivia with a distinct hostility to the US eradication programme. Regrettably resurgence in coca plant growing and the production of cocaine was reported in Latin America 2005.

- Reduction in opium poppy production in Mexico. Heroin consumption is a re-appearing problem in the USA and there are signs that the drug traffickers have been concentrating their efforts on opium poppy crops in both Mexico and Colombia. There are clear signs of increased production in Colombia although over 8000 hectares were destroyed, with US Government help in 1999. However, the production in Mexico was reduced by nearly two thirds. These two countries produce only 6% of the world's total opium poppy but are of major US concern because of their proximity to the US markets.

- Drug Syndicates have suffered. With the co-operation of key, governments the drug, trafficking syndicates in the Western Hemisphere have suffered major reverses and do not enjoy the relative immunity which the Cali and Medellin cartels had in the 1980's. In October 1999 a joint effort between the US and Colombian governments, code named "Operation Millennium" resulted in the arrest of scores of major Colombian traffickers and a major international trafficking network was disrupted. In Mexico, the government continued its activities against the powerful Juarez cartel and in 1999 law enforcement and military units moved against the remnants of the Carrillo Fuentes Organisation. The Mexican government formally indicted a State Governor who had been co-ordinating multi-ton shipments of cocaine from Colombia to the Yucatan peninsular for onward shipment to the USA and Europe.

Promoting International standards.

As part of the long-term anti-drug strategy, the US government has laid claim to many successes around the world in assistance given to the reform of legal systems, law enforcement training, the strengthening of judicial systems, and the improvement of banking and financial systems. Extradition treaties have been created or improved, resulting in a fear amongst drug lords that their immunity from prosecution has been removed and that they are liable for prosecution and imprisonment in the United States when convicted. In November 1999, the Colombian authorities extradited a Colombian citizen to the USA for the first time in 9 years. Other countries that extradited nationals to the USA were Mexico and Pakistan.

Progress against international money laundering. Without the ability to move illicit money into legitimate financial and commercial activities drug profits lose much of their attraction and spending power. Drug trafficking generates many millions of dollars and it is not easy to dispose of vast amounts on money, which have to be weighed rather than counted. Several countries have a reputation for a willingness to connive at illegally obtained funds, and some go out of their way to encourage traffickers to bank with them. However, great advances have been made in improving world banking systems and it has become much more difficult to launder drug profits to the extent that the traffickers are now obliged to spend as much time and money in 'legitimising' their funds as they do to producing and transporting drugs. One of the requirements of the 1988 UN Convention is that subscribing countries take measures to introduce legislation, which prevents money laundering. Several countries have been encouraged and assisted in drafting appropriate legislation and the US Government has worked closely with its international partners in focussing on expanding collective measure to make it more difficult for the drug trade to move its assets, especially into offshore financial institutions. The ultimate aim is to exclude drug money altogether from the international financial system. Another financial measure that is encouraged is the use of seized trafficking assets in the fight against the international drug lords.

Restrictions on Precursor Chemicals. One of the major growth areas in the illicit drug market has been with the production of dangerous synthetic drugs. Amphetamine Type Stimulants (ATS) are appearing around the world because they are relatively easy to produce and because young people have been duped into believing that they are neither addictive nor dangerous. These stimulants are an important and highly lucrative element in the international drug market and have overtaken cocaine and heroin as the drugs of choice in some regions. In particular "Ecstasy" is very popular. Synthetic drug production allows the traffickers to control the total process from manufacture to marketing and it is an extremely profitable business, which can be developed by the diversion of commercial chemicals known as precursors. The production of opiates and cocaine require the use of widely available chemicals but the production of ATS requires the use of precursors that have few legitimate uses and which are therefore traded in smaller quantities. The US Government and its partners have had significant successes in encouraging producer countries to introduce regulations, which control but do not inhibit legitimate use. A multilateral system of information exchange on chemicals has been developed. Customs and law enforcement agencies around the world have been taught to recognise legitimate shipments and to look out for unusual or excessive consignments of precursor chemicals. This has reduced the availability of precursors and has made life more difficult for clandestine manufacturers. Many illegal laboratories have been destroyed with the DEA seizing 1,916 methamphetamine laboratories in continental USA in 1999. However, some countries leave the regulation of these chemicals to the government departments responsible for trade. The function of these departments is to promote rather than inhibit trade and therefore there is a reluctance to disclose information gained from domestic commercial companies to those departments responsible for promoting international chemical regulations.

Influencing Political Will. Some countries are cynical enough to exploit aid and co-operation programmes while at the same time they connive at the necessary reforms that will inhibit drug trafficking. If the political will is weak in the face or organised crime then it is not long before both the government and the administration become corrupted. Thus, a basis for US Government counter-narcotics policy has become the bolstering of political will to oppose the illicit drug trade; this policy has paid dividends where political leaders have had the courage to protect the long-term political and social well being of their country. Where that political will has been absent, drug cartels have flourished and the reasons for this are clear for all to see. The drug lords command immense wealth which they use to subvert even relatively strong societies. In some areas their power to corrupt has made it possible that an elected government may consist in the future of totally corrupt and unprincipled leaders who actually promote the drug trade as part of their national policy. An average figure for the US street price of a metric ton of pure cocaine is $100million and this can be multiplied by a factor of 3 if it is cut with adulterants. Annually the US seizes approximately 100 metric tons of cocaine, which would be worth $10billion to the cartels. Given that it is thought that the majority of the illicit drugs imported into the USA are not seized by law enforcement agencies, these remaining supplies produce revenues, which outstrip the budgets of many individual countries. In the financial year 2000, the US Government's overall budget for international drug control operations was approximately $1 billion – the equivalent of just 16 metric tons of cocaine. The drug cartels can afford to lose vast amounts of money in pursuing their trade. In the same way that drug lords seek to corrupt democratic leaders so too must right thinking governments, seek to assist and support those threatened governments to resist the drug trade. The USA claims some success with its international partners in achieving this end.

Next Steps:

Whilst the significant achievements claimed by the USA and acknowledged by international partners are valid and have made an impact on the illicit drug trade, no-one should be under the illusion that they are anywhere near enough to achieve the UN aim of a 'World without Drugs'.

Sadly, many ill-informed people continue to advocate the legalisation of drugs without having a clear knowledge of what damage these views are doing to world economy and the wellbeing of nations. These efforts need to be consolidated and developed regularly if the drug traffickers are to be defeated. In 2003 the UN reaffirmed its determination to pursue the anti-drug philosophy set out in the UN Conventions and UNGASS 1998.

Not only must there be a continuous drive to achieve drugs demand reduction but also the targeting of supplies and suppliers has to be continuous. Crops must be eradicated, illicit laboratories need to be decommissioned, precursor chemical flows must be disrupted and disabled, and financial havens must be abolished; no stage of the process can be neglected. At the same time, every effort must be made to protect the livelihood of those farmers who have come to depend upon the coca and opium crops, by providing them with alternative income sources.

Governments must be encouraged to tighten financial controls, improve their oversight mechanisms, enact and enforce money laundering legislation and identify better ways of pursuing the illegal assets of drug traffickers and traders. Full use must be made of International Economic Emergency Powers to keep the drug trade from exploiting legitimate companies for their criminal purposes.

A great deal of knowledge and experience has been accumulated in the fight against drugs and the thrust during the 21st century must be to consolidate and share that knowledge with well-intentioned governments so that they can become more effective and active partners in the fight against drugs. It is also necessary to isolate those governments, which fail to comply with their international obligations.

Non-participating countries must be persuaded that it is in their long-term interests to co-operate otherwise international sanctions must be introduced to compel compliance with UN Conventions and internationally agreed, standards of conduct. Where help is needed, it must be provided and where sanctions are appropriate, they must be enforced. Even with the most determined efforts, it is unlikely that the international drug trade will be seriously disabled for several decades, if then. Resistance has to be relentless if continuing harm is to be diminished and eventually reduced to non-critical proportions.

NB - The source for much of the information on US policy is the International Narcotic Control Strategy Reports published annually by the Department of State Bureau for International Narcotics and Law Enforcement Affairs.

CHAPTER 10
" A Drug-free World – We Can Do It! "

Pino Arlacchi, an Under Secretary General, and then the Executive Director of the UN Drug Control Programme, closed the Special Session of the UN General Assembly, held in New York in June 1998 entitled 'Countering the World Drug Problem Together', with the optimistic, and many would say unrealistic, statement about achieving a drug-free world.

In the context of at least thirty years of an unprecedented proliferation of drugs to hitherto unimaginable proportions, and in a world where mind-altering substances have been used in many different cultures for centuries, it seems naïve to believe in the concept of total eradication of the drug problem. More realistically, it would be sensible to speak of aiming for an internationally agreed, co-ordinated and sustained effort to reduce the enormity of the problem to more manageable proportions.

The Secretary General of the United Nations – Kofi Annan reinforced this message in 2006 when he said on 21st June, designated the International Day against Drug Abuse and Illicit Trafficking:

> "Taking drugs or not is about making choices -- informed choices. Yet too many people in the world are badly informed about the potentially devastating effects of drugs. That is why we need to work for better education and greater awareness to prevent drug abuse. We need more consistent leadership from Governments. We need better examples from role models whose drug use damages more people than just themselves. We need to spread the understanding that drugs are illegal because they are a problem; not a problem because they are illegal. Drugs cause health and mental problems. When addictive, they can spell misery for users and those close to them. When taken intravenously, they can spread deadly disease -- especially HIV/AIDS. When they wreak their devastation, they respect no boundaries of income, race, occupation or geography. Our efforts must focus especially on young people -- through outreach, peer-to-peer networks, and using opportunities such as sport to keep young people active, healthy, and confident. That also means engaging and encouraging parents and teachers to play their part in full. Our efforts also require working to reduce supply -- through law enforcement, and through working with the producing countries to give farmers sustainable alternatives to growing illicit crops. In this way, we must strive to tackle poverty and drug supply at the same time."

Certainly, drugs have become an International pandemic disease, and this is recognised by the UN and the many countries which have been signatories to various conventions, protocols and agreements all aimed at diminishing, if not eradicating, the problem. Unfortunately, we are nowhere near achieving a united, international and comprehensive response in terms of defining the exact nature and the ramifications of that 'disease' and identifying effective antidotes. Indeed there has been pressure to revisit the UN Conventions and to amend them in less restrictive ways. Several European countries have changed their stance against drugs by effectively decriminalising the personal possession and use of small amounts of cannabis, and there is demand for the same approach to be adopted for other drugs such as ecstasy and ATS.

A former United States Drug 'Czar', General Barry McCaffrey likened the drug problem to cancer: -

> "Dealing with cancer is a long-term proposition. It requires the mobilisation of support mechanisms — medical, educational, and societal — to check the spread of the disease and improve the prognosis. The symptoms of the illness must be managed while the root cause is attacked. The key to reducing both drug abuse and cancer is research driven prevention coupled with cutting-edge treatment" (US National Strategy Document, 1999)

Pino Arlacchi chose the analogy — "the International Community is a doctor facing a deadly disease. Drugs — quite simply — kill people. And it is our responsibility to find the cure".

The analogy to cancer and disease is apt, because like cancer, drugs have penetrated deep into the daily lives of countless millions of people, afflicting all and killing many. Like cancer, the word 'drugs' can strike terror into some people's minds. This is not only because the substances are themselves dangerous and addictive, but also because the methods adopted by ruthless traffickers to perpetuate their trade are made deliberately terrible, in order to reinforce their deadly influence and to maintain their power.

According to the Secretary General of the UN, Kofi Annan, (World Drug Report 1997), there were 21 million 'victims' around the world who abused heroin and cocaine, and 30 million who abused amphetamine-type stimulants. In 2005, the UNODC estimate of the total number of people worldwide thought to abuse drugs stood at 200 million (World Drug Report 2006). These figures represent an enormous affliction not only of the victims but also of their families and friends, and the numbers of abusers are increasing in many areas. Drug abuse is a terrible 'disease' which is growing more rapidly than the spread of AIDS. Preventing drug use is the only way to eliminate drug-related harm; any illegal drug use is drug abuse that should not be tolerated.

The UN proposals to defeat drugs.

The Special Assembly in New York was intended to be the occasion when the International community found common ground in the mission to create a momentum towards a drug free world in the twenty-first century.

The Assembly adopted an action plan based on 'Guiding Principles of Demand Reduction' as the foundation for its initiatives. This plan together with measures proposed to enhance International co-operation to counter the drug problem, represented a 'balanced approach' which would attempt to address the responsibility of nations where consumption as well as those where production is a problem.

It suggested methods of stemming the flow of stimulants and their precursor chemicals; achieving judicial co-operation internationally; combating money laundering; and collaborating on crop eradication and the means of alternative development where drug plant crops such as coca, poppy and cannabis, are destroyed. This "new vision" was described as "a quantum leap from the piecemeal and pilot projects of the past three decades".

The Political Declaration accompanying the plan summed up the UN perception of the global drug problem: -

> "Drugs destroy lives and communities, undermine sustainable human development and generate crime. Drugs affect all sectors of society in all countries; in particular, drug abuse affects the freedom and development of young people, the world's most valuable asset. Drugs are a grave threat to the health and well-being of all mankind, the independence of States, democracy, the stability of nations, the structure of all societies, and the dignity and hope of millions of people and their families."

The problem remains not so much in the definition as in identifying and applying appropriate and co-ordinated remedies around the world. So far, this book has described the scale of that problem. What remains to be achieved as a matter of extreme urgency is to examine the proposals and to add to them where they are deficient. In the early stages, it is thought to be more appropriate to find a significant form of treatment that will diminish a 'deadly disease' to a more manageable 'ailment' with the ultimate aim always being to strive to achieve abstinence in a non-drug abusing world.

This book has given an indication of how serious the global problem of drugs has become; the reasons for this are numerous. A significant factor, which has allowed the cancer to take such a strong hold, has been the failure on the part of governments and the international community, to recognise in time, the strength and determination of the 'drug-pushers'. They have also failed to recognise the 'denial' that has existed in societies in refusing to anticipate the dreadful consequences of human weaknesses and the culture of tolerance and acceptance of illicit drugs, even by those who have no intention of using them personally. Further it is obvious that there is a serious deficiency in the provision of treatment for those who need it.

The World Drug Report for 2006 indicated 3 ways in which further action is deemed to be essential:

> "Countries need to do more to reduce drug demand in general and to target ATS and cannabis in particular. The profile of the users of these drugs differs from that of those who use heroin and cocaine, and treatment appropriate to their needs is still not widely available.

> There is an urgent need to prevent the spread of HIV/AIDS among injecting drug users, whether they are street addicts, sex slaves or prison inmates.

> While drug market trends are moving in the right direction, more work is needed to ensure that these trends are sustained. After so many years of drug control experience, we now know that a coherent, long-term strategy can reduce drug supply, demand and trafficking. If this does not happen, it will be because some nations fail to take the drug issue sufficiently seriously and pursue inadequate policies. In other words, each society faces the drug problem it deserves."

Demand Reduction.

This approach is an obvious priority, which was endorsed by the UN as the basis for much of its future efforts to defeat drugs. The problem is that it is not simply a matter of 'educating' drugs out of societies. Demand and supply reduction must go hand in hand and the methods adopted in different regions must take account of local cultures and traditions, which should be respected, except where they are inherently harmful. Persuading people to abandon something, which they may have practised for centuries is not always an easy task and there may be a deep-rooted antipathy to change.

This approach must work hand in hand with other methods of dealing with drug abuse and must encompass co-ordinating law enforcement, social work, education, readily available treatment and public health information. The criminal justice system must be adapted to distinguish between those who need punishment and those in need of treatment and has a role to play in referring users to appropriate treatment without necessarily blighting them with a criminal record. Education must address not only drugs, but also associated problems such as health, sex, and the vulnerability of youth to all kinds of social difficulties, which may be exacerbated by taking mind-altering substances. Cultural change for the worse must not be allowed to develop because society has neglected to set and maintain standards; a laissez-faire attitude to the development of young people into adulthood must not be permitted. Social welfare must take account of, and address the causes of drug abuse. Public health must address the collateral problems caused by drug abuse and must provide adequate and readily available treatment.

Each discipline must be interrelated and must collaborate in an identified and agreed approach to the whole problem of drugs. Add to this the need for each country to understand the problems of its neighbours and to adjust its initiatives to achieve a common international good rather than just dealing with local problems in a locally convenient way. Demand reduction is an all embracing concept which, so far, the developed countries have failed to prioritise and adopt fully; the problems for the developing world are much more difficult to address.

One of the guiding principles of demand reduction for the UN is the concept of 'shared responsibility', which supports a comprehensive, balanced, and co-ordinated approach by which supply control and demand reduction reinforce each other. The policies recommended are aimed at preventing the use of illicit drugs and reducing the adverse consequences of drug abuse by encouraging all responsible individuals and all countries to recognise and to combat the harm.

The long-term intention is to sustain a mutually supportive system based on international agreements that share common aims and agreed remedies. Demand reduction programmes should cover all areas of prevention. Not only should initial use of non-medical drugs be discouraged but also the reduction of adverse health and social consequences should be addressed through education, treatment, counselling, rehabilitation, after-care and social reintegration.

All those in need of assistance must be given ready access to appropriate services, which collaborate with one another in handling the primary objective of demand reduction. Such collaboration needs to be replicated at government level and the information regarding these efforts must be widely publicised and readily available. All efforts to reduce the abuse of drugs must be part of a comprehensive and broad social policy initiative that is constantly evaluated and adjusted to take account of both experience and changing trends. Policies must be credible, and easily understood and should become an essential part of every government strategy both centrally and locally.

Currently we are nowhere near achieving that state of affairs. A new form of thinking is vital if we are to make any impact on this essential aim of world wide demand reduction.

Crop Eradication and alternative development.

Another of the aims of the UN Special Session was to achieve the elimination or a significant reduction by 2008, of crops of the coca bush, poppy plant, and cannabis varieties. Special attention should also be given to reversing the growing trend in abuse and production of psychotropic substances, and this would include targeting synthetic drugs and the precursor chemicals necessary to produce them. If the idea of eliminating plant crops became substantially successful, there would be an inevitable 'displacement' to a demand for synthetic drugs.

This strategy is not as straightforward as it may seem. Mention has been made of the large numbers of people around the world whose livelihoods have come to depend upon the production of the drug producing plants often because they are marginalised and neglected people. There is too the sheer scale of the problem to be considered. Again, mention has been made of an area in Latin America the size of the North American landmass, much of which is devoted to producing coca bushes and poppy plants for cocaine and heroin. In Afghanistan, the estimated crop of opium for 1999 was 4600 metric tons and in the current state of that country, such an amount could be easily exceeded in the future. In 2003 poppy production was enormous and although the yield did not match that of 1999 it was not far removed and despite international declarations there is little sign of success in reducing the crop. The crop in 2004/5 was equally large. In Burma (Myanmar) and elsewhere, similar problems arise although it was reported in 2004 that the leader of the Wa tribe had promised to eliminate poppy plantations within one year (The Times May 1 2004); that had not been achieved by 2006. However, in 2005 it was reported that the production of ATS to replace the locally diminishing supply from the opium poppy crops had increased significantly in both Myanmar and China. In the same year the US Government identified Myanmar as a country that had failed during the previous 12 months to adhere to its obligations under International counter-narcotics agreements

One sure way of creating social unrest, to the point of driving the peasants into the arms of the narco-terrorists of Colombia and other Latin American countries, is to take away the means of earning their living, without providing an equally rewarding crop-replacement scheme. Money well spent by the terrorists and drug dealers has aligned the interests of the peasant farmers with their own. It will take a significant amount of international funding and intelligent assessment of viable and sustainable markets to set up programmes that will realign those interests with the aims of the UN Conventions.

At least one Latin American country made a determined effort to comply with the UN resolution to eradicate the coca crop. In Bolivia, thought to be the third largest producer of coca after Colombia and Peru, and second only to Colombia in the production of cocaine, the President announced his intention of eliminating all coca production by 2002. With huge International support and assistance from the UN Drug Control Programme, Bolivia managed to destroy 12000 hectares of the crop in the first 8 months of 1999 and claimed to be on course for total eradication by the end of 2001. After 1997 the government received $800 million in International aid and achieved some success by paying coca farmers $3500 for every hectare of voluntarily destroyed coca plantations. Farmers were required to register for compensation and the longer they waited before doing so, the less they received in payments. It was reported that there was a reduction to only 27000 hectares of coca plantations.

For every 10,000 hectares of coca that is eradicated, it is estimated that there will be a reduction of 100 tons of cocaine. However, at a meeting in Washington DC in November 1999, drug control experts from the Americas met at the Western Hemisphere Drug Policy Leadership Conference. These experts expressed their concerns that despite such initiatives as occurred in Bolivia and Peru, South American drug production was still buoyant and was thought to be recovering from initial cutbacks in production (International Police Review Jan/Feb. 2000).

In March 2000, it was reported that some peasant farmers were involved in 2 weeks of rioting in the capital La Paz in protest against their loss of income brought about by the crop eradication schemes. Riot police had to restore order by the use of tear gas and baton charges. (BBC News 24 March 31st 2000). In May 2001, there were a number of demonstrations by the coca growers urging the President to reverse the eradication policy and there were threats of further disorder if their demands were not met.

Bolivia was once the world's third biggest producer of coca and the early indications of the American induced crop eradication plan looked promising, but now one in four Bolivians is out of work and with coca production significantly reduced the peasants claim that they have nothing to sell. This situation resulted in civil unrest.

Late in 2001, there were almost daily marches on the capital, La Paz where the poor farmers conducted violent demonstrations against the Government policy. Ironically, despite the crackdown on the coca crop, cocaine consumption in the USA and Europe remained high because Colombia increased its production to fill the gap in the market.

Many Bolivians feel that the eradication programme was an unmitigated failure and that they have been suffering for nothing. Many peasants returned to growing coca (The Observer 16.9.01). In the Presidential elections of 2002, the head of the coca-growers union finished a close second. Evo Morales and his political coalition, the

Movement to Socialism (MAS) also finished as the second largest political force in the new Congress. This result left indigenous and leftist parties controlling more than 30% of the 157 seats in Congress, which meant that it became difficult to continue with US driven counter-drug policies in Bolivia. In the Presidential election in December 2005, Morales became the clear winner and he announced his intention of reversing the US driven coca eradication scheme claiming that growing coca for traditional use is different from cocaine production.

It has to be borne in mind that the coca plant will grow in the most adverse conditions and will allow three or four harvests a year. Most alternative crops would require more favourable growing conditions than for the coca bush, and would need tending and fertilising. Given that a substantial part of Colombia (as much as 50%) is controlled by narco-terrorists, it is difficult to imagine how they could be persuaded to give up such a lucrative source of income, without mounting an all out war. This would be difficult to win and expensive to conduct, with no certainty that it would not become another prolonged and frustrating conflict.

A similar problem continues in Afghanistan where all provinces are involved in growing the opium poppy. It has been estimated that 66% of the GDP of Afghanistan depends on the production of opium/heroin. Many of the poor are totally dependent upon the opium poppy for their livelihoods and in the short term it seems highly unlikely that alternative crop development programmes will be successfully introduced there.

It would be necessary for the wealthier members of the International community and World Financial Institutions to consider ways in which millions of people could be either retrained, re-financed or subsidised for a good standard of living if there is to be any realistic hope of successful 'alternative development'. This initiative would take massive amounts of money to be provided in such a way as to avoid incurring compounding, world debts for the third world countries. Clearly, there is insufficient funding at present for alternative development at national and international levels. A major rethink of global finances would be necessary for such a proposal to be effective. Governments and international organisations will need to co-operate to ensure that all relevant communities affected by the illegal drug economy are able to achieve sustainable and legitimate livelihoods.

If the proposed crop elimination schemes were to be successful, and it is reasonable to assume that they would not be in the short-term, those schemes would need to be integrated with effective law enforcement measures to ensure that those who risked continuing production would be penalised. Success of alternative development programmes would depend upon long-term political and financial commitment of the governments of the affected countries and the International community.

International research and development programmes would need to assess the most suitable types of alternative crops for specific regions and it would be necessary to ensure that world markets were willing and able to absorb the supplies of the new crops. Without very sophisticated research techniques and the introduction of a sophisticated system of marketing, as things stand at present, such a universal state of affairs would be extremely difficult to achieve, particularly in the given time-scale set by the UN. Nevertheless, after an initial phase of simple crop substitution that was too narrow, it was expanded to include more sophisticated socio-economic development plans. These new measures included food security, off-farm income generation, re-training, education, health care, road construction, and micro-credit schemes. These have led to some improvements.

However, major problems have arisen because of insufficient research and planning or the mismanagement of certain schemes. The case of Laos is mentioned because the eradication of the opium crop is reported to have caused specific social problems for indigenous people. According to an article published in the New International Magazine (November 2004) many H'Mong and Akha hill people were dying because of an over-zealous implementation of the global anti-narcotics campaign. There were said to be few alternative income-streams and because of eradication programmes more than 30000 have been displaced from their traditional homes and mountain habitats and resettled in valleys. Crop substitution and aid has been made in only a few areas. According to one NGO survey, people from all age groups are dying from malaria and dysentery partly because of the lack of suitable sanitation and sufficient medicines. A separate UN Report is quoted that observes that resettled hill people 'not only lack sufficient rice, but face fresh diseases - malaria, gastro-intestinal problems and parasites which are seldom experienced in the mountains'. It appears that the eradication programme has been poorly researched and is being mishandled in an unseemly haste to meet artificial deadlines.

Whilst it may be possible, with determined International collaboration, to achieve such changes over a longer period of time than a decade, the implications of this particular proposal are enormous. Currently there are vast areas of the world where such development programmes are necessary and desirable and where there is no drug-crop production.

There are political, legal, cultural, social, economic and ecological considerations, which vary from region to region. In some areas of the developing world the infrastructure and the basic understanding of what has been proposed, is limited. To achieve such an optimistic, yet very necessary objective would require massive International training and aid packages, which would be enormously costly. To gain universal co-operation and acceptance of the proposal would require diplomacy and persuasion of a very high order.

The chain is only as strong as its weakest link'. Internationally there will have to be a total rethink of the way in which world trade is conducted and finances are managed; priorities will need to be re-assessed in all countries and there is not much evidence of a willingness to embark on such an undertaking. For whatever reason, world leaders do not yet consider drugs to be a sufficiently important issue and the financial power of the drug lords and International criminal organisations, remains a formidable opposition to such propositions.

When the Soviet Union broke up and communism ceased to be the only system by which people were governed, many people who had not liked the system, and yet were secure and guaranteed both a job and an income, felt suddenly threatened by the 'free market' system and "globalisation". Change within a society sometimes takes a generation to achieve; it requires both education and experiment before the younger generation accepts as normal, that which is anathema to its parents and grandparents. It is likely that the alternative development schemes, as proposed at the UN Special Session in New York, will require a similar amount of time and education before they can hope to take effect. Ten years was too optimistic a target.

Countering Money Laundering

It is estimated that over $500 billion or 2% of the global GDP is illegally laundered each year and most of this stems directly from the proceeds of drug trafficking. Unlike other businesses, drug trafficking can 'afford' to be inefficient and can absorb losses that would put others out of business, in order to make their money appear legitimate.

The drug lord, Pablo Escobar was thought to use up to 60% of his vast income for corrupt purposes in facilitating his trade. Money laundering is on the increase and represents a major threat to the stability of countries and whole world regions. Traditional money markets are vulnerable to the movement of unimaginably large amounts of cash from one to another at the touch of a computer key.

Global capital represents immense power and the world threat is enhanced when weak or corrupt governments see advantage in engaging in, or conniving at laundering. Moves towards free trade and the process of growing economic co-operation by International governments have facilitated the easy transfer of funds to the great advantage of the traffickers.

The global free-trade economy established by the World Trade Organisation is dominated by unaccountable, trans-national corporations which have few loyalties to any particular community and are both willing and able to move at will wherever the financial conditions are most advantageous. Within this context, many International criminal organisations have assumed a 'legitimate' business front.

Inadequate regulation has led to some banks and financial institutions becoming active participants in money laundering schemes. One observer has noted that even some legitimate banks have an incentive to connive at money-laundering because they need to compete with other banks that face fewer regulations in their own States. They are commercially challenged as well by those banks and global funds, which operate 'offshore' and effectively outside any system of regulation.

('Drug Politics - Dirty Money & Democracies' David C Jordan 1999.
See also International Narcotics Control Strategy Reports for 1999 & 2000.)

In 1998, the US prosecuted 3 Mexican banks, CONFIA, SERFIN, and BANCOMER and 26 Mexican Bank officials for laundering millions of dollars derived from illegal drug trafficking. Additionally, bankers from two Venezuelan Banks, BANCO INDUSTRIAL DE VENEZUELA, and BANCO DEL CARIBE were charged in the money-laundering scheme. The undercover investigation resulted in the seizure of over US$98million, $67 million from bank accounts and $31million in cash seized from traffickers, as well as 4 tons of marijuana and 2 tons of cocaine. BANCOMER and SERFIN each pled guilty and forfeited $16million to the Government as well as being fined $500,000. CONFIA settled the indictment with a civil plea and forfeited $12million. $64million of the $98million was forfeited to the US Government.

(INCSR 2000)

The collapse of the International bank, Bank of Credit and Commerce International (BCCI), which had such International repercussions, was, in large measure, due to involvement with the criminal laundering of drug profits. Even the Vatican bank, Banco Ambrosiano was linked with drugs. In February 2000 two people appeared before a court in New York and admitted laundering up to US$7billion through the Bank of New York; some of this was thought to be the proceeds of drug trafficking.

(BBC World News 17.2.2000, The Times 18.2.00)

It was reported (The Sunday Times 20.2.00) that in Britain the National Criminal Intelligence Service (NCIS) warned the Prime Minister that within two years it was likely that London would become a major target for money launderers. It has been estimated that the Russian Mafia is currently passing upwards of £20billion p.a. through British banks. There is every indication that the NCIS prediction was correct.

The UN Special Session agreed to the proposal that those countries which had not adopted money-laundering regulations, should undertake to make a special effort to implement the provisions against that practice outlined in the UN Convention Against Illicit Trafficking in Narcotic Drugs and Psychotropic Substances 1988, by 2003. This would include passing laws to make money laundering a criminal offence, and adopting counter-measures to prevent International criminal gangs from finding safe havens and having access to their illegal funds. Authorities should take steps to identify suspicious financial transactions and to take measures to trace, freeze and seize the proceeds of illegal drug trafficking. In the last decade, some countries have been very successful in using the seized proceeds of drug traffickers in funding drug counter-measures.

The UN recognised that this proposal would require very sophisticated harmonising of International legislation for it to be effective. It acknowledged that the International attempts to liberalise financial markets to attract legitimate investment were being damaged by money laundering activities, but it did not mention its awareness, if any, that liberalisation of financial markets was actually facilitating criminal activity. However, it did state that one of the ways in which the drug trade's effectiveness could be diminished would be for the removal of "bank secrecy impediments to efforts directed at preventing, investigating and punishing money laundering'.

Clearly, such measures are necessary if the UN effort to move towards a 'drug-free world' is to be successful. The difficulty lies not with the good intention of the world powers, but with those smaller countries, which have neither the power nor the inclination to adopt the proposals. The drug trade dominates some countries either because their staple money making crops are drugs related or because there is distinct advantage in deriving huge incomes from drug trafficking.

A former US Ambassador to Peru, David C Jordan has pointed out that, some countries have an interest in "protecting" the drug trade. Sometimes this interest arises because the proceeds of drug trafficking provide much needed foreign exchange, assists in servicing national debts (often to the World Bank), or because there is political advantage derived in preventing a greater gap between more and less well developed nations. There are also benefits in using these illicit funds towards weakening a rival power or in financing political ideals such as FARC in Colombia, or simply in maintaining a political elite in power with all the privileges that such wealth can bring. (Drug Politics – David C. Jordan, 1999). Sometimes, the governments of drug producing countries are "victimised" by the criminal cartels through corruption and intimidation.

In all of these situations, it is extremely difficult to imagine any willingness on the part of such governments to change without significant inducements or support from the International community. It should be noted that the very things that the developed countries are seeking to achieve in furthering legitimate trade also facilitate drug trafficking and inhibit some of the UN proposals. Again, a major rethink is necessary.

Other UN proposals for Demand Reduction:-
Amphetamine Type Stimulants and Precursor Chemicals.

Any reduction in the availability of plant crops for the production of drugs is almost certain to promote an increase in the abuse of Amphetamine Type Stimulants (ATS) which are already a significant problem in many areas of the world, although almost non-existent in others. Regrettably, awareness of this problem is not yet universal and the responses are uncoordinated, despite the fact that globally a greater number of people are dependent on ATS than on heroin and cocaine. The UN Special Session advocated that a much greater awareness of ATS should be promoted and collaborative efforts should be taken Internationally to inhibit their production and trafficking.

In many countries, the main abusers of ATS are young people who regard the substances as being relatively harmless and risk-free; the abuse of ATS became an accepted part of mainstream culture in the rave and club scenes of the western world. This raises the need for international research and collaboration in ways of preventing the further development of this cultural change and of inhibiting the manufacture and supply of the illicit substances. There is a need to prevent the diversion of laboratory equipment and the chemical materials (precursors) which form part of a legal, inter-regional trade and which are used in the illicit manufacture of ATS in clandestine laboratories. Such prevention requires the co-operation of manufacturers, suppliers, customs, and inter-governmental agencies. Significant moves have been made to encourage such co-operation but large amounts of chemicals are still finding their way to illicit drug manufacturing laboratories.

The term 'designer drugs' was coined some years ago because of the ability of chemists to alter the formula of recognised drugs in a slight way or to use substitute chemicals such that the new drugs may not be covered by prohibitions. This chemical flexibility enables the production of new ATS very rapidly and this, in turn, raises the need to share information between co-operating states to enable them to react to the developments.

Measures to Promote Judicial Co-operation.

The remaining recommendation of the Special Session was that as far as possible, all States should co-operate with one another to ensure the smoothest possible arrangements for extradition, mutual legal assistance, and the transfer of proceedings between states. Exchange programmes between law enforcement agencies and joint training exercises together with the exchange of information and criminal intelligence were encouraged, as were controlled deliveries between states to enable drug traffickers to be more easily arrested and their organisations disrupted.

The peculiar problems associated with maritime law and the interdiction of drug shipments at sea were addressed as were other complementary measures designed to ensure the safety of judges, prosecutors and law enforcement officers in their often dangerous tasks against drug trafficking. States were generally encouraged to share their knowledge and experience to ensure that best practices could be adopted universally.

What more must be done: -
Any successful drug policy depends upon three things:-

- Prevention and Education aimed at promoting healthy lifestyles for everyone;

- Treatment that is immediately available and affordable for those who have the misfortune to become drug dependent or affected by drug associated diseases;

- Intelligence driven and compassionate enforcement aimed at public safety but also supporting prevention and treatment by acting as a deterrent to drug use and as an influence towards treatment participation

There is a seemingly insatiable appetite for drugs around the globe. International free trade policies accommodate money laundering. Substantial regions of the world depend upon the drug trade for the survival of vast numbers of people, and some governments see advantage in facilitating the drug trade or the laundering of money through offshore banking systems which inhibit investigation and the tracing of assets.

There is a huge amount of ignorance and misunderstanding about drugs. Drug trafficking is not considered by any government to be its major priority. The United Nations has drawn attention to these problems but has neither the power nor the resources necessary to address them in anything like an adequate manner.

In a desperate plea to the International community, Pino Arlacchi said in his closing address to the Special Session of the UN General Assembly in New York – "Our work cannot simply be left on a piece of paper in this conference room". This was, perhaps, a more realistic observation than that about the possibility of a drug-free world.

Several times attention has been drawn to the need for a massive rethinking of global priorities if any more substantial impact is to be made in reducing drug trafficking. It is also necessary to take stock of national and domestic thinking in all countries. Several additional courses of action seem obvious and may be divided into International and National measures to be adopted in the desire to reduce drug abuse and drug trafficking.

Internationally: -

Compliance with Conventions. Although most countries have ratified international conventions, some do not comply and many are introducing arbitrary policies to address local problems that cause difficulties for others. There is no enforceable system to compel compliance and so the United Nations should update these conventions and secure agreement for the introduction of sanctions against those countries who either do not comply or who trade knowingly with countries that promote or connive at drug production and trafficking. There is an increasingly strong connection between organised crime, terrorism, and drug trafficking. This must be addressed by all countries being prepared to condemn without exception all that participate in state sponsored terrorism. An international system to enforce compliance with laws against organised crimes, money laundering, terrorism, and drug trafficking must be negotiated and introduced. Similarly, because corruption is endemic in many countries the UN should supply an agreed definition of corrupt practices against which other world organisations can measure compliance with loans from the World Bank and IMF. Unless international partners impose strict conditions the problem of drugs will grow and spread out of control.

An International Research Institute should be established under the auspices of the UN to study the social, economic, cultural and political forces that engender drug trafficking. It should produce an accurate template for achievable, multi-national actions. Additionally this institute should be supplied with accurate statistical information together with information on all measures taken in the assault on drug trafficking. Suitably qualified and experienced international workers to evaluate information and assess policies should staff the Institute. It should make recommendations for any necessary changes to the Conventions. The Institute should award degrees, research-bursaries and become the World Centre for information, evaluation, and advice on drug matters. This Institute should validate and accredit appropriate training packages for drug workers and should offer advice on appropriate material for educational institutions. A corollary of this must be that all International bodies should subscribe to the Institute and should adopt recommended programmes for use domestically wherever possible and appropriate. An annual report should be issued with an account of any successes or failures. The internal accountability of the UN must be established such that a culture of complete openness and honesty prevails rather than attempting to satisfy the peccadilloes of individual donors. Failures are extremely valuable lessons and should not be covered up for the sake of reputations or appearances.

The Institute should collaborate with other research agencies to ensure that accurate information is shared and that appropriate research is encouraged in the field of treatment and pharmacology.

Funding the Institute must be by way of a regular allocation of money or by precept from member countries. Important research must not be restricted by voluntary donations.

Regular International Convention on Financial Matters under the auspices of the UN should be created, and backed by sanctions against any country, which fails, without good reason, to implement its terms. Drug trafficking and the laundering of the proceeds present a real threat to global financial stability. Too many countries permit the development of questionable Offshore Financial Centres, which facilitate deception and protect the criminal. "Ultimately, the concerted joint effort of regulators, law enforcement officials, and regulated licensed professionals working closely with those providing financial services in all jurisdictions will be necessary to combat financial crimes, including money laundering and tax evasion, while diminishing the perceived potential threat of the offshore financial sector to global financial stability".

(International Narcotics Control Board Strategy Report, 2000).

There must be total International acknowledgement that drug trafficking adversely affects the whole world, and therefore the control of drugs should be identified as a key, policy requirement in International agreements, protocols accords, and conventions. No country should enter any agreement with any other country, which is intentionally in breach of the international initiative against drugs. All aid packages should carry a condition requiring active measures in demand and supply reduction by the country receiving aid. Appropriate sanctions should apply against any breach of an ethical anti-drug policy. Loans from the International Monetary Fund should be dependent upon good practice against drug trafficking by the recipient countries.

A Drug Control Agency should be encouraged/established in each country so that a law enforcement network can be established to share intelligence and to act in unison to interdict major drug traffickers particularly, but not exclusively in regions close to the major drug producing countries.

Liaison officers should be sent to essential areas to assist in gathering intelligence, assisting developing countries to deal with their problems, and assisting in the interdiction of criminals and illicit drugs around the world.

A statement of common aims and objectives to tackle law enforcement, education and training, and treatment should be adopted internationally so that common approaches are taken wherever possible. A greater commitment should be made to bring all countries to acceptable standards in terms of enforcement, the sharing of intelligence, treatment and public health information. Education should be directed not just a school pupils but must include all those whose job brings them into contact, either directly or indirectly, with illicit drugs. This must include doctors and medical workers, teachers, social workers law enforcement personnel, and of course, parents and grandparents. There must be a commitment to the prevention of drug use as this is the only way to ensure a progressive approach to the elimination of drug related harm.

Crop Eradication/Alternative Development Schemes must be thoroughly researched and backed by sufficient funding and training to enable those who have become financially dependent on growing coca or poppy crops to benefit from sustainable alternative means of income and support.

Nationally: -

Drug Control must be made a continuing national priority to which significant funding and resources must be applied, not only in addressing the conditions likely to promote drug abuse, but also to ensure a balanced policy. A three pronged strategy based on targeted and intelligence led enforcement, accurate and effective education not only of children and young persons but also anyone whose work requires knowledge of drugs, and readily available treatment and counselling for dependants and their families. Nothing should be done that either promotes or accepts, encourages or facilitates the abuse of drugs. No government policy should in any way perpetuate a situation where drug dependent people are allowed to remain chemically dependent; every initiative should be aimed at abstinence and healing. No policy should be followed that gives rise to the impression, particularly amongst the young, that drug use will be tolerated. This sends out dangerously mixed messages to young, vulnerable and impressionable minds.

An Office of National Drug Control Strategy, adequately funded and staffed by appropriately trained people must be established in each country, with the power to compel Government approved demand/supply reduction initiatives etc. The Chief Executive of this office to co-ordinate all government policies, activities, and funding in the campaign for demand/supply reduction schemes.

A U.K. Drug Institute should be funded and established at one of the leading universities to gather accurate information about drugs, carry out research, maintain and evaluate statistics, and analyse the effectiveness of policies and drug related projects. The institute should work in conjunction with the International Research Institute.

Demand reduction should become a major initiative in domestic policy. Clearly, there is a pressing need for the government to adopt a serious policy about drugs and to introduce legislation that will address the problem in every area. There must be a nationally required core syllabus on drug education at every stage from kindergarten through to tertiary level. All teachers' Training Colleges should include drug awareness information as part of the syllabus. The workplace is another area in which appropriate legislation should be introduced to compel appropriate policies, including testing where necessary. Every family unit must be provided with adequate, accurate and easily understandable information about drugs so that informed discussions can take place in the home environment. It would be sensible to provide evening classes for parents with a nationally approved and standard syllabus.

Supply Reduction must continue to be part of an anti-drug strategy with targeted, intelligence led enforcement and co-operation between all relevant agencies. There should be a national clearing house of intelligence and as far as possible both international and national co-operation should be co-ordinated.

Harm Reduction should be defined in such a way that it excludes the possibility of it being used in a way that promotes or tolerates drug abuse. The ultimate aim of all government policies must be ultimate abstinence by those unfortunate enough to be drug dependent. It should become a criminal offence to advocate or promote the use of illicit drugs and the misuse of legal drugs.

Training must be compulsory for people who are responsible for others; thus all teachers, social workers, police officers, doctors, health workers, prison officers etc should receive adequate and accredited training from packages approved by the International Research Institute. A professional qualification for those who work in the drug field is highly desirable and the aim should be for this to become essential.

Public Education - the government should pursue a continuous and high profile public health education scheme to inform the public about drugs.

Employment in Central and Local Government. All employees of Central and Local government should be required to give an undertaking that they will remain drug-free – backed up by appropriate and random testing, particularly for those involved in safety and security matters. All applicants for employment with Central Government should be subjected to pre-employment screening/testing. Both Central and Local Governments should insist that any organisation with which they enter into a contractual agreement should demonstrate that it has suitable anti-drug policies in place; failure to give such a guarantee should result in the contract negotiations being abandoned.

Tax benefits should apply to all companies, which adopt government approved strategies in the working environment.

A National Parents' Council similar to the Parents' Drug Corps in the USA should be established to assist parents to understand and deal with the problems of drugs and to act as a catalyst for updating legislation and procedures for dealing with drug problems.

Treatment. There must be sufficient and readily available treatment centres available for those unfortunate enough to need them. (See "The Costs and Benefits of Substance Abuse Treatment. Findings from the National Treatment Evaluation Study (NTES)" August 1999.) Experience in the USA and to a lesser extent in the UK has shown that treatment can be very effective and that every effort should be made in the workplace, the criminal justice system and in communities to encourage drug abusers to become drug free. This applies especially in prisons.

The Criminal Justice System must be able to distinguish between those who need treatment and those who require punishment. Every Prison must have a nationally agreed treatment programme combined with appropriate sexual health policies, which are capable of being continued by those who require it after release. Drugs should not be tolerated in the prison system. The Government should extend the offering of treatment and rehabilitation of offenders as an alternative to imprisonment with open-ended sentencing for those addicts who must be imprisoned or who decline the treatment alternative; release following upon them achieving abstinence. Drug courts, drug testing, and follow up treatment/counselling within the criminal justice system can reduce drug consumption and recidivism. One of the goals of the system must be to help people with drug problems renounce crime and become productive and motivated tax-paying members of the community. Education and training for work must be an integral part of all treatment within the criminal justice system. All drugs must be excluded from prison establishments except those administered by medically qualified staff on authorised prescription.

The sale of cannabis seeds and cannabis-growing accessories and any drug related paraphernalia should be prevented by new legislation.

Alcohol and tobacco products must be included as targets for demand reduction.

Conclusion

Despite some extraordinary and commendable efforts by many dedicated people who are determined to reduce the harm caused by drugs; and despite the identification of many of the problems and remedies by international bodies such as the UN, the initiatives against drugs are often disparate, fragmented and frequently, non-effective. This global problem does not yet have sufficiently high priority with governments for the UN proposals to be effective.

Far too much ill-informed comment and ignorance exists about drugs so that now we are witnessing a massive cultural transition from almost total abhorrence to that of tolerance and acceptance of dangerous drugs as a normal part of life. People who see great advantage in the legalisation of addictive substances actively encourage this change in public attitude.

If we care enough about the future of our young people and the stability of the International community, then all Governments must do much more than they are at present. It is necessary to give anti-drugs policies the priority, which will ensure that the facts are fully understood and are not distorted or ignored because the problem has become "too difficult".

Drugs intrude everywhere from the classroom to the boardroom; from the factory floor to Government Offices. Every Government Inspectorate should be required to emphasise the need to address the problem of drugs. It is a major threat that requires a major and permanent response.

Drug affliction has blighted all societies and has become everyone's problem. All of us must make the effort to ensure that we are aware and that our representatives are aware, of this galloping cancer, and show a determination to develop and sustain demand reduction in all areas of our lives.

Priorities must change and international collaboration must emphasise the defeat of this sinister and spreading global problem as being equal in importance to any other consideration. Without such a commitment, the alternative is a serious diminution of the standards and wellbeing of the global community.

APPENDIX I

Conclusions and Recommendations of a Report to the Winston Churchill Memorial Trust in November 1986 entitled "An Examination of some Drugs Education Programmes in North America" by Dr Ian OLIVER: -

- The obvious and most significant conclusion is that either drugs awareness education or skills for living programmes are an essential element in all schools and should be introduced throughout the UK as soon as possible.

- It would be foolish to ignore the needs of parents and the support that they can give to such programmes and so it is essential that information programmes be prepared for parents.

- Denial is still a problem in the USA and it is most certainly a problem in the UK. Every effort should be made to overcome this by convincing people that to acknowledge a problem is not a reflection on them either as teachers or parents and that to ignore the existence of a potential for drug abuse is one sure way of establishing that abuse.

- Education cannot start soon enough and although the concentration of effort appears to be necessary for the 12/13 year age group, instruction in kindergarten and at university level is necessary – there must be a continuation of education.

- The teachers must be good role models and must be properly trained before they attempt to instruct such programmes. A programme is only as good as its presenter.

- It would be a valuable exercise to conduct a national and independent research into the true extent of drug abuse in the UK.

- It would seem to be valuable to consider the establishment of regional or national "hot-lines" on the free-phone system which would enable people, concerned in any way, to contact a centre either for advice and guidance, or merely, to allow them to pass on any information that they may wish.

"Drug Affliction" Select Bibliography:

A

The Classification of Cannabis under the Misuse of Drugs Act 1971.
Advisory Council on Misuse of Drugs (ACMD) March 2002.

Hidden Harm: Responding to the needs of children of problem drug users.
ACMD 2003.

Reducing Drug Related Death – Report ACMD.

Swiss Heroin Trial AESBACH Ernst. Swiss Doctors Against Drugs 1998.

B

Killing Pablo. BOWDEN Mark, Atlantic Books 2001.

Drugs in Sport. British Medical Association 2002.

Waiting to Inhale. BOCK Alan. Seven Locks Press 2000.

HIV/AIDS and Drugs Misuse in Russia. BUTLER William E, 2003.

"The Therapeutic Use of Cannabis" BMA Report -18.11.97.

C

Clued Up – A Handbook on Drugs for Gay Men.
Camden & Islington Community Health Services.

Bad neighbour Policy: Washington's Futile War on Drugs in Latin America.
CARPENTER Ted Galen

International Perspectives to the Prosecution of Drug Traffickers.
Paper delivered to International Assn of Chiefs of Police Conference,
Dublin 9th May 1999 by CHARLETON S.C.

International Drug Trafficking: Law Enforcement Challenges for the next Century.
CONSTANTINE Thomas – Paper delivered at International Assn of Chiefs of
Police Conference, Dublin 9th May 1999.

Hemp for Health. CONRAD Chris. Healing Arts Press 1997.

Buzzword. COOK Walton, Public Policy Press 2001.

Driven by Drugs: US Policy Toward Colombia.
CRANDALL Russell. Lynne Reiner 2002

D

The Pursuit of Oblivion. DAVENPOT-HINES Richard.
Weidenfield & Nicholson 2001.

The Truth About Drugs. DIXON Patrick. Hodder & Staughton 1998.

The Selfish Brain. Du PONT Robert. American Psychiatric Press Inc 1997

America's Longest War: Rethinking our Tragic Crusade Against Drugs.
DUKE Steven B and Gross Albert C.

Drugs of Abuse. Drug Enforcement Administration USA.

Guidelines for a Drug Free Work Force (2nd Edn) DEA 1998.

Speaking Out Against Drug Legalisation. DEA 1994.

Protecting Young People – Good Practice in Drug Education in Schools and Youth
Service. DfEE 1988.

Drug Prevention in Schools – Circular 4/95. DfEE.

Drug Education – Curriculum guidance for Schools. DfEE May 1995

Drug Education – Getting the Message Across. DfEE 1998.

Innovation in Drug Education – Drug Proof. DfEE 1997.

A Digest of Drug Education Resources for Schools. DfEE 1995.

Get it Straight – The Facts about Drugs. DEA

"Team Up" A Drug Prevention Manual for High School Athletic Coaches. DEA.

Assessing Local Need: Planning services for Young People.
Drugscope and Drugs Prevention Advisory Service.

An Ounce of Prevention A Pound of Uncertainty.
Drug Policy Research Center 1999.

Drugs: Guidance for Schools DfES/0092/2004.

E

Funding Evil. EHRENFELD Rachel. Bonus Books 2003

The White Labyrinth: Cocaine and Political Power. ENSSELAER III Lee R. Transaction Publishers, New Brunswick 1991.

Drug Legalisation – For and Against. EVANS Rod L, BERENT Irwin M. Open Court 1992

Speaking Out Against Drug Legalisation. Drug Enforcement Administration 1994.

F

Starting a Drug Free Business Initiative.
FAY Calvina L. Houston Drug Free Business Initiative.

The Good News about Drugs and Alcohol. GOLD Mark. Villard Brooks NY 1991.

Drug Crazy. GRAY Mike. Random House 1998.

Cannabis. GREEN Jonathan Pavillion 2002

Access to HIV Prevention, Global HIV Working Group May 2003.

Grampian Police Substance Misuse Policy Document 1996.

H

Developing Local Drug Strategies.
HMSO 1998.Tackling Drugs to Build a Better Britain.
UK Government Drug Strategy CMND 3945 1998. Updated Drug Strategy 2002.

Tackling Drugs Together – A Strategy for England 1995-1998 HMSO

Drug Misuse and the Environment. Home Office 1998.

In the Arms of Morpheus HODGSON Barbara. Greystone Books 2001

The Government Drug Policy: Is it Working? House of Commons Home Affairs Select Committee Report 22.5.02 HC318-1

A follow-up evaluation of Project Charlie – A Life-Skills drug education programme for primary schools.
HURRY Jane, LLOYD Charlie, Home Office Paper 16 – 1997.

House of Commons Select Committee on Science and Technology
– "Drug Classification: making a hash of it? HC1031 31.07.06

I

International Police Review Magazines

International Journal of Drug Policy

J

Drug Politics. JORDAN David C. University of Oklahoma Press 1999.

Drug Consumption Rooms – Report of Independent Working Group – JOSEPH ROWNTREE Foundation May 2006.

K

Prodigal Soldiers. KITFIELD James Brassey's1995.

L

After Prohibition. LYNCH Timothy, Cato 2000.

Cognitive Dysfunctions in Chronic Cannabis Users LUNDQVIST. T An Integrative Approach. Dissertation. Stockholm: Almqvist & Wiksell International; 1995.

America Assesses Needle Exchange Programmes. MAGINNIS Robert L, Family Research Council, Washington DC 1997

Rising Phoenix. MILLS Kyle, Harper 1997.

Marijuana as Medicine? The Science Beyond the Controversy. MACK Alison, JOY Janet. National Academy Press 2001.

The Fix. MASSING Michael, Uni of California 2000.

Testimony of the Director of ONDCP (USA) before the House Government Reform and Oversight Committee – Drug Legalisation 16th June 1999. McCAFFERY Barry.

The Politics of Heroin. McCOY Alfred. Lawrence Hill Books 1991

War on Drugs: Studies in the Failure of US Narcotics Policy. McCOY Alfred, BLOCK Alan. Westview Press 1992.

The American Disease: The origins of Narcotics Control – MUSTO David F; New Haven: Yale University Press 1973.

Merck Manual – 2nd Edition Drug Use during Pregnancy.

N

Confusions about alcohol and other drugs.
National Institute on Drug Abuse (NIDA) USA 1999.

Illusions. National Child Safety Council – USA.

Marijuana & Medicine. Edited by NAHAS G.G. et al. Humana Press 1999.

O

High Intensity Drug Trafficking Area Strategy Reports
– Office of National Drug Control Policy USA(ONDCP).

US National Drug Control Strategy Reports 1995-2005. ONDCP

Drug Education in Schools. OFSTED Reports 1997, 2005.

An Examination of Some Drug Education Programmes in North America.
OLIVER Dr I.T. – Report for The Winston Churchill Memorial Trust 1986.

P

Drugs and the Law. Police Foundation Report 2000.

Police Review Magazines.

Blow. PORTER Bruce. St Martins Griffin 1993.

Portuguese Drug Strategy Documents – 1999.

The Safer Injecting Handbook (1st Edn) PRESTON Andrew, DERRICOT Jon.
Martindale Pharmaceuticals.

Alcohol, Drugs and Tobacco – Prevention Handbook.
Pompidou Group Council of Europe 1998.

R

Adverse Health Consequences of Cannabis Use: A Survey of Scientific Studies Published up to and including Autumn 2003. RAMSTROM. National Inst. Of Public Health, Sweden.

Taliban. RASHID Ahmed. IB Tauris 2000.

Royal College of Physicians – Cannabis and cannabis-based medicines Potential Benefits and Risks to Health – Report of Working Party 2005.

The Harm Reduction Model
– RILEY Diane, Harm Reduction Network Printing 1996

The Laundreymen. ROBINSON Jeffrey. Pocket Books 1998

S

Cocaine Politics: Drugs, Armies and the CIA in Central America. SCOTT Peter Dale, Jonathan Marshall Uni of California Press 1991.

Cocaine. STREATFIELD Dominic. Virgin 2001.

Pharmaceutical Care of the Drug Misuser
– Scottish Centre for Post Qualification Pharmaceutical Education.

Drugs & Young People in Scotland. Scottish Health Education Group, 1986.

The Right Response – Managing and Making policy for Drug related incidents in Schools. SCODA 1999.

The Right Approach – Quality Standards in Education. SCODA 1999.

Guidance on Selecting Drug Education Materials for Schools. SCODA 1998.

Cannabis as a risk factor for psychosis: systematic review SEMPLE David M et al University of Edinburgh, Journal of Psychopharmacology 19(2) (2005) 187-194.

A Rational Approach to Drug Prevention in the Primary School: Practice Review and Policy Developments. STOKER Peter. Early Child Care & Development Vol 139 pp73-97, 1997.

Early Years Drug Prevention and Education: Getting back on track. STOKER Peter. Early Child Care & Development 1999.

Action in Partnership. The Scottish Office.

The UK Threat Assessment of Serious Organised Crime for 2006/7 by The Serious Organised Crime Agency).

T

False Profits: The Inside Story of BCCI – the World's Most Corrupt Financial Empire. TRUELL peter, GURWIN Larry. Boston: Houghton Mifflin 1992

U

Global Illicit Drug Trends 1999-2004. UNDCP/UNODCP.

Guiding Principles of Drug Demand Reduction and Measures to Enhance International Co-operation to Counter the World Drug Problem. UN 1998.

Single Convention on Narcotic Drugs, 1961 UN

Convention on Psychotropic Substances 1971 UN

Convention Against Illicit Traffic in Narcotic Drugs and Psychotropic Substances UN 1988

UN. Convention on the Rights of the Child, article 33).

General Assembly Special Session on Drugs Report UN 1998.

Progress Report on the mid-term review of UNGASS by the Executive Director, 8.4.03 UNODC/ED/2).

International Criticism of the Swiss Heroin Trials.
UN International Narcotics Control Board Report 1999.

International Narcotics Control Board Reports 1999-2004.

International Narcotics Control Strategy Reports 1999-2005 US Dept. of State.

Precursor Chemicals – Reports INCB 1999-04

Tajikistan Human Development Report 1998 UN

UK Anti-Drug Co-ordinator's Reports 1998-2000.

UK National Plan 1999/2000.

UK Performance Targets for 2005 and 2008

USA National Drug Control Strategy Reports 1995-2005.

UN World Drug Reports 1997-2005

HIV & AIDS Health Promotion – An evolving strategy.
UK Health Depts. Nov 1995.

UNAIDS Report 1999-04.

Drug Abuse Prevention in the Workplace and the Family. UNDCP.

Drug Misuse at Work – a guide for Employers. UK Health & Safety Executive.

Drugs – The Business Agenda. Royal & Sun Alliance/ UK Government.

A Parent's Guide to Prevention – Growing Up Drug Free. US Dept of Education.

What Works – Schools Without Drugs. US Dept of Education 1986.

V

Drugs, Sport & Politics. VOY Robert MD. Leisure Press 1991

W

World Drug Reports 1999-2006 UNODC

From War to Work: Drug Treatment, Social Inclusion and Enterprise.
YOUNG Rowena. The Foreign Policy Centre 2002.

Z

Is Marijuana the right Medicine for you?
ZIMMERMAN Bill, BAYER Rick, CRUMPACKER Nancy. Pocket Books UK 1999